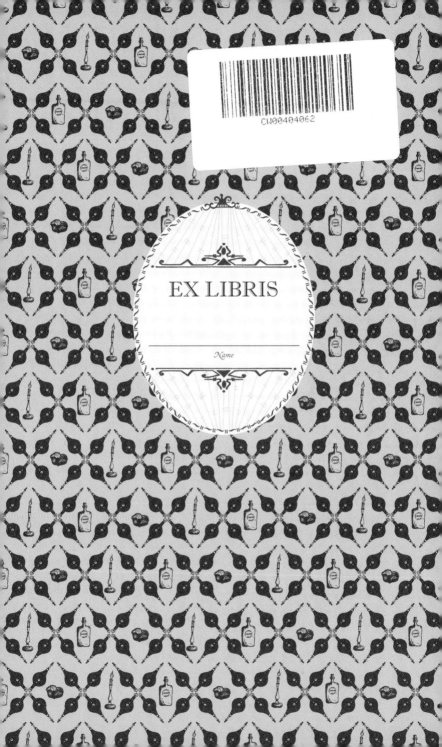

EX LIBRIS

Name

Bleeding, Blisters & Opium

JOSHUA DIXON

AND THE

WHITEHAVEN DISPENSARY

MICHAEL SYDNEY

Stainburn Publications
6 Brierydale Lane
Stainburn
Workington
Cumbria
CA14 4UH

stainburnpublications.co.uk

ISBN 978 0 9563881 0 0

Design and cover illustration by karensawrey.com
Printed and bound by Verité CM Limited (veritecm.com)

For Loraine

This Portrait of

JOSHUA DIXON M.D.

Copied and Drawn upon Stone by S. Crosthwaite from the original Picture in the
Whitehaven Infirmary Painted by George Sheffield.

Is respectfully inscribed by Permission

To the Right Hon the Earl of Lonsdale, K.G.

By the Publisher

Published by R. Gibson, Whitehaven.   Aug.st 1830.   Printed by C. Hullmandel, London.

JOSHUA DIXON. *Lithograph by S. Crosthwaite 1830. Based on a portrait by George Sheffield, Wigton.*
Wellcome Library, London.

Bleeding, Blisters & Opium

JOSHUA DIXON
AND THE
WHITEHAVEN DISPENSARY

MICHAEL SYDNEY B.Sc. M.B. F.R.C.P.
General Practitioner, Whitehaven

'*T*HE crown and glory of 18th century medicine is that it first attempted to bring such knowledge as it had to the service of the mass of the people. The rich Physician, pampering to the imagined ills of the wealthy, has been taken as typical of the age, but he is common to all ages; the new figure was the dispensary doctor risking his life daily in the disease-ridden hovels of the poor.'

M.C.Buer, 1926, *Health Wealth and Population in the Early Years of the Industrial Revolution.*

CONTENTS

INTRODUCTION

THE town of Whitehaven in the North-West of England has a rich architectural, industrial and maritime history, which has attracted much attention. Less appreciated is its equally rich medical history. Many people are aware of the existence of the Whitehaven Dispensary, but few are aware of its work in bringing medical care to the sick poor of the town. The Dispensary Physician, Joshua Dixon M.D. attracts but one line in Daniel Hay's *Illustrated History of Whitehaven*, being described as 'one of the best-loved men who ever practised medicine'. In 1983, a booklet produced by the West Cumberland Health Authority celebrated the 200th anniversary of the founding of the Dispensary in 1783. This described Dixon's Annual Reports as 'a model of their kind'. Harry Fancy gets a little closer in Poverty and Health in Eighteenth-Century Whitehaven, published in 1986 for the Friends of Whitehaven Museum. This includes the Dispensary Annual Report for 1807, the founding of the House of Recovery at the Ginns in 1819, and the tribute paid to Joshua Dixon by his sons, following his death in 1825.

Yet, in Joshua Dixon, Whitehaven possesses a figure of immense historical significance, not only for the town, but also for the history of Medicine. Dixon's uniqueness lies in the fact that he served as the only Physician to the Dispensary for forty years. His legacy lies in his meticulous Annual Reports, a medical and social record of life in Whitehaven in the late eighteenth and early nineteenth centuries. Data from these reports was quoted in a major Pathology textbook almost a century later. Dixon's medical reputation spread across the country. His charity and philanthropy for the poor of Whitehaven gave him an iconic status in the town. I hope this book will reflect Dixon's life and work and help to re-establish the reputation he so richly deserves.

Much of my research for this book was completed in the Cumbria Record Office and Local Studies Library in Whitehaven, and it is a pleasure to record my thanks to the staff for their help, support and enthusiasm. Special thanks are due to Lesley Park, Mary Chisholm, Catherine Clark, and the Local Studies Librarian, Jenni Lister. I experienced similar qualities in my visits to the Record Offices in Carlisle and Newcastle, to the Jacksonian Collection in Carlisle Public Library, and to the Museum Collection in the Whitehaven Beacon. I am grateful to the Beacon Curator, Charlotte Stead for permission to use material from the Museum Collection, and to the Cumbria Record Office and Local Studies Library (Whitehaven) for allowing me to use documents held in the Library, including the Dispensary Annual Reports, and the extracts and inserts from the *Cumberland Pacquet*, which appear in the text. In all extracts the spelling, grammar and style of prose, including the use of the 'long s' are those of the eighteenth century. The Dispensary Annual Reports for 1783 and 1821 are reproduced in full.

I received information and encouragement from Maureen Fisher and Bob and Betty Marshall from the Lamplugh and District Heritage Society. Steve Matthews from Bookcase in Carlisle suggested a change of emphasis to the book, for which I am grateful. Gloria Edwards, Richard and Meredyth Bell read an early draft and provided helpful comments. Mark Megan, Practice Manager in my day job, helped me out of several tight technological corners. I appreciated advice and encouragement from Melvyn Bragg, Michael Moon, Margaret Crosby from the Whitehaven News, and Alison Considine of St. Bees School. The Wellcome Library in London readily gave me permission to use illustrations from their Images Collection. My sincere thanks go to Julia Evans for her expert copyediting and proofreading, and to Karen Sawrey for her inspirational authentic design. My dogs, Lucie, Hollie and Abbie gave me their own special qualities on the fells whilst I mentally rehearsed my prose. Finally my heartfelt thanks go to my wife, Loraine, who, in addition to computer skills, gave me much love and encouragement during the writing of this book, and introduced me to the concept of a deadline.

PROLOGUE

A Child's Death

THE scene unfolding before him was all too familiar to the Physician. He knew that the child's death was now very near. For two days, each breath had been a contest between the child's weakening intercostal muscles and diaphragm, and the insidious grey membrane occluding her throat, slowly choking her to death. Three days ago, when the cough first began, the Physician had seen the beginnings of the membrane, and knew what it meant. He had watched, helpless, as the noisy respirations quickened and the child's eyes became wild with terror. He had kept vigil with the child and her mother for a day and a night, tensing with the ebb and flow of each laboured respiration. Now the tiny heart, visibly pounding against the thin chest wall, was failing, and death was near. The Physician reached over to place a few more drops of laudanum on the dry protruding tongue of the exhausted child. Slowly, slowly, slowly, the terrible noisy breathing softened. The fear in the child's eyes receded as she slipped away into unconsciousness. Her breathing became shallow and quietly stopped. Joshua Dixon looked into the wet eyes of the child's mother. Without a word, he picked up the limp body of his infant daughter from his wife's lap, and laid it gently on the coverlet. Husband and wife embraced. God was good. Next year would bring another child. Later, leaving his wife, Anne, in the candlelit room, beside the body of their first daughter, the Physician hurried away into the December night. His friend, the Revd. Wilfrid Huddleston, Vicar of the Old Chapel, St. Nicholas, would need to know of tomorrow's burial, and there were still patients waiting to see him in the Dispensary.

JANE DIXON,
fifth child of Joshua and Anne Dixon.

Baptised April 17th, 1784.

Buried at St. Nicholas Church, Whitehaven, Christmas Day, 1784.

WHITEHAVEN
IN THE ERA OF
JOSHUA DIXON M. D.

THE town of Whitehaven, in Cumberland, holds a unique place in seventeeth and eighteenth-century history. Over a period of less than one hundred years it rose from the obscurity of a small fishing village to, arguably, the second most important port in England, after London. The three main factors in this development were coal, tobacco and the Lowther family.

The earliest settlement, around 900 A.D. was established at the mouth of a small creek, between two headlands of St. Bees sandstone, into which the Pow Beck flowed. Whitchaven became part of the Manor of St. Bees, and was acquired as part of that estate by the Lowther family in 1630. In 1634, Sir John Lowther obtained titles to the coal, saltpans and tenants of the estate, which at that time numbered about twenty-four households. Sir John left the estate to his second son, Christopher, who inherited the title in 1637. Sir Christopher began exporting coal and salt to Ireland, and, in 1634, built the first pier to shelter the

A BIRD'S EYE VIEW OF WHITEHAVEN. *Matthias Read 1738.*
From a Photograph, courtesy of The Beacon, Whitehaven.

shipping using the port. Sir Christopher died in 1644, and the title passed to his infant son John, who inherited it on his majority in 1660.

Sir John Lowther was interested in town planning, and, as the sole landowner, was able to put in place his vision of a gridiron plan for the streets and houses of the town. Lowther Street was planned as a broad avenue, leading from Sir John's mansion, The Flatt, to the lower town around the harbour. The old chapel situated in the line of the planned street, was demolished and replaced with a new church dedicated to St. Nicholas. Once Lowther Street was in place, other streets were laid at right angles and in parallel. Sir John Lowther was responsible for major developments in the coal trade of Whitehaven. He acquired coal bearing land on the outskirts of the town, and expanded the trade with Ireland. By 1700, seventy-nine ships were carrying coal to Ireland, mainly to Dublin. Most ships were less than one hundred tons weight, and made five or six return journeys each year. Sir John also had a commercial interest in the developing tobacco trade in the town. In 1683, a Whitehaven vessel, The Resolution, with a keel length of only sixty feet, voyaged to Virginia in search of tobacco. Sir John had an eighth share in the vessel. The tobacco trade with Maryland and Virginia quickly established Whitehaven as one busiest ports in England and contributed to the rising prosperity of the town. At the same time, ships from Whitehaven established links with Jamaica and Montserrat in the West Indies. These voyages were long, arduous and fraught with danger from pirates, shipwreck and acts of war. The ships sailed south to the coast of Guinea to pick up consignments of slaves, before making the journey across the Atlantic. The slaves were exchanged for a cargo of sugar or tobacco. By the time of Sir John's death in 1706, Whitehaven had grown into a town of over 3,000 inhabitants.

Sir James Lowther, Sir John's second son, inherited the estate in 1706. His elder brother Sir Christopher had been disinherited because of an unacceptable marriage and his dissolute ways. Land in King Street and on the East Strand, which had been earmarked for industrial development by his father, was now made available for further house building. In 1711, to counteract competition from increasing maritime trade in Parton, a small village to the north of Whitehaven, Sir James built an extension to the old pier, and built a new mole extending out from the end of Duke Street. A second church, Holy Trinity, was built in 1715, at the junction of Scotch Street and Irish Street.

Sir James Lowther was largely an absentee landlord, whose main commercial interest was the collieries. Sir James relied on his local agents, the brothers John and Carlyle Spedding to look after his commercial interests. Under their occasionally devious stewardship, exports of coal reached 50,000 tons in 1717, and following a temporary recession, had risen to 90,000 tons by 1735. During the 1740s

Whitehaven reached the peak of its prosperity. At this time, Whitehaven was supplying seventy per cent of Ireland's total coal imports. By 1800, this had fallen to twenty-eight per cent. South Wales and Lancashire had become serious rivals to Whitehaven, and there was significant local competition from Workington, Harrington and Maryport.

The tobacco trade with Maryland and Virginia increased quickly in the early years of the eighteenth century, with an annual average of 1.5 million pounds weight of tobacco being imported. The union with Scotland in 1707 allowed ships from the Clyde to enter the lucrative tobacco market, and as a result Whitehaven suffered a temporary drop in imports. By 1730, trade had recovered, and tobacco imports were reaching two million pounds per annum, much of which was re-exported to Ireland, Holland and France. In 1743, ten million pounds of tobacco were re-exported. By now, there was a significant dynasty of powerful tobacco merchants in Whitehaven, including Peter How, Walter Lutwidge, William Gale and Richard Kelsick. In 1746, Whitehaven could claim to be the second largest tobacco port in England after London.

This period of prosperity was short lived. The relative prominence of the harbour was already declining in favour of larger river-based ports. The harbour at Whitehaven was not deep, and could only accommodate vessels of shallow draught. Whilst this was adequate for the smaller collier vessels, which made frequent short trips to Ireland, larger vessels built for the transatlantic trade were unable to use the port. During the time of the expanding coal and tobacco trade, Whitehaven lacked a significant capacity for complementary economic growth. The town was cut off to the east by the Cumbrian fells, with low population, poor communication and few local industries. Attempts were made to develop industries to provide goods for export – glass bottles, bricks and salt, for example – but these were of limited success. There was no ready local market for much of the imported goods, which then had to be re-exported. Whitehaven lost out to rivals such as Liverpool, Bristol and Glasgow where there was room to expand the ports, and a developing industrial hinterland to support trade. After the Seven Years War, the tobacco trade with France declined in favour of the Clyde and the Thames. By 1760, it had almost disappeared. Several of the Whitehaven tobacco merchants, including Peter How and the Lutwidges became bankrupt.

The important census of 1762, gives the population of the town as 9,063. This census lists the owners and occupiers of each house. Houses were graded into front houses, back houses, cellars and lofts. The gentry, merchants and professional men lived largely in the vicinity of the eastern end of Lowther Street, in Queen Street and Roper Street. Cellar dwellings were concentrated in the older lower lying parts of the town near the harbour. Front houses were occupied by professional men and merchants, whist the cellars were the abode of the labouring population.

By 1767, the town had reached the limits of its development, being bordered by the grounds of The Flatt to the East, the hill of Bransty to the North, and the steep slopes behind the harbour to the south of the town. Little land was available for new building. Although the relative prosperity of the harbour had declined, coal mining and ship building continued to flourish, and the population continued to grow. New homes were built on every available space, particularly the spacious back gardens of the larger town houses. These were in filled with cramped housing. Houses were subdivided and sublet as lofts, middle floors and cellars.

In the late eighteenth century two important housing developments occurred. Sir James Lowther had died unmarried in 1755, and the estate had passed to another branch of the Lowther family, Sir James Lowther of

WHITEHAVEN FROM BEHIND CORKICKLE, EARLY 19TH CENTURY. *Mount Pleasant &*
Hogarth's Chapel are visible in the central distance, with the New Houses on the left. Courtesy of Michael Moon.

Lowther, who became Earl of Lonsdale in 1784. In 1788, Lord Lonsdale planned a development of 500 houses off Preston Street for his colliery workers. In fact, only 270 of these New Houses were built. Around the same time, James Hogarth, a local linen manufacturer, built 117 out of a planned 200 dwellings on a steep slope to the south-west of the town, an area known as Mount Pleasant. Hogarth was an uncompromising noncomformist character. A broadsheet published in 1788 gave notice to all his tenants:

> That he is fully determined no idle disorderly Persons, who bring up their Children without SCHOOLING and WORK shall dwell in his Premises. He promises to erect a Charity School and a Church to accommodate them on the LORD's DAY; which he will insist on all his Tenants frequenting, or else they must depart from his Premises.

The houses at Mount Pleasant were built in three terraces on the side of a hill, without drains or sewers, so that the roads and houses quickly became damp. The water supply was inadequate for the residents and often failed in summer. The New Houses had only twenty-one ash pits for the 270 houses, so that contamination with human waste was common and animal waste was simply left to rot. Despite this, these developments were considered a major improvement for the town, and attracted favourable praise from Joshua Dixon in his Annual Reports. In 1807, Dixon states, 'The New Houses have a very pleasing appearance, and a delightful situation with regard to air, light and prospect.'

The conventional view of eighteenth-century Whitehaven is that depicted in 'A Bird's Eye View of the Town', the famous 1738 painting by Matthias Read. It shows spacious streets and gracious houses. Dr. William Rollinson quotes Sir Nicholas Pevsner in describing Whitehaven as the 'earliest post-mediaeval planned town in England', adding that it must be also the first planned town of the Industrial Revolution. Further developments included the building of St. James Church in 1753, on a hill at the north end of Queen Street, and the mansions built at the eastern end of the town by the prosperous merchants of the time. As the century progressed, the population of the town increased from 9,063 in 1762, to 16,000 in 1785. There was no land for new building in the latter part of the century and the town became divided into three distinct areas. To the east around the landward end of Lowther Street, towards The Flatt, Scotch Street, Irish Street and Queen Street, were the spacious houses of the merchants, professional men and sea captains. Towards the harbour, a pattern of tenements, cellars and squalid overcrowded accommodation prevailed, with a raucous background of inns, coffee houses and the bustle of the port. Mount Pleasant and the New Houses occupied the high ground to the south of the town, built ostensibly as a philanthropic gesture for the colliery and linen workers, but without any regard for the necessities of clean water and good sanitation.

Joshua Dixon, in his Annual Report of 1807, offers the following description of the town:

> WHITEHAVEN, in latitude 54 32 North, longitude 3 30 West, has not improperly been styled the *Montpelier* of the *North*. The health of its inhabitants has been preserved by various advantages peculiar to its situation. The soil is sandy and dry; and, though the hills on each side and opposite the harbour are lofty, the sea shore is considerably elevated. The coast is remarkably bold and rocky; abounding with marine vegetables, whose exhalations must afford a copious supply of vital air.

> The town is situated at the head of the Vale, which leads to St. Bees, and the communication with the sea, at its furthest extremity, a range of four miles, occasions a regular supply, and indeed a constant stream of fresh air; the immediate effects of which are gratefully felt in sultry weather; as its salutary influence must undoubtedly operate at all seasons; and to this

circumstance alone the healthy state of *Whitehaven* and its vicinity has been attributed.

The town is so contiguous to the sea that the tide flows up to it. With regard to the interior (a circumstance of no small consideration to the well-being of the inhabitants of any populous town) *Whitehaven* is remarkably well built; the dwellings are generally commodious and comfortable. The houses, with very few exceptions, are of free stone, covered with slate. There is not a tiled, nor a thatched roof in the town. Many of the streets are spacious; and most of them crossing each other at right angles, the Ventilation (another important matter) is preserved clear and uninterrupted; in short, the principal streets are completely ventilated by the north-west and south-east winds, and the opportunity which the inhabitants have of recreating themselves by their occasional walks on the noble piers, which form the HARBOUR of WHITEHAVEN, contributes still more to the salubrity of the place.

Sea-port towns from the constant effluvia of *burning tar* are observed to be more healthy than the interior country. This, *Whitehaven* enjoys, of course, only in common with other maritime places of trade; but it possesses other advantages, which are not extended to all such places. It is situated in the neighbourhood of extensive COLLIERIES and LIMEWORKS; and the bowels of the earth also contain great abundance of free stone, slate, and iron-ore. The limestone is burnt in the neighbourhood, and carted through the central streets, in large quantities , for exportation; and the coals, which are of excellent quality, are the only article of fuel.

But the occupation of the numerous, highly useful and ornamental Rows of Houses, (each two stories in height) built upon the rising ground to the westward of the town,(in which every poor family, employed in the coal-works, possesses a separate, convenient, and rent-free habitation) has conduced most effectually to the general salubrity of this place.

Considerable benefit likewise may be derived from the frequent application of fresh-prepared *white-wash*; which is strictly attended to in the houses briefly described above. These buildings amount to three hundred; and, from the uniformity of their ſtructure, and the cleanliness of their exterior, they make a very pleasing appearance.

This adjunct of the TOWN of WHITEHAVEN is not yet diſtinguished by any other name than that of The *New Houses*, (all of which are numbered) except the Front Range, which is called *Caſtle Row*, possessing one of the moſt delightful situations, both as to *air, light* and *prospe_ct_*, that is to be met with in this part of the country.

We have had several proofs of infectious fever being accidentally introduced into a single house; which from indiscreet conduct spread to many families in town; when by the usual precautions, not an individual in those extensive buildings, has suffered the leaſt symptom of disease.

Several alterations have lately been made, which cannot fail of contributing as well to the health as to the convenience of the inhabitants;--such as widening the lower end of *Duke-Street*, where it joins the *North-Tongue*;--the fine spacious approach to the *North Wall*;--the commodious new Road from Branſty; the entrance to which from the town, will shortly be completed;-- and the enlargement of the Road and the excellent Pavement of the *New Town*.

The improvements now forming in the town, and the conſtruction of its additional buildings, will also, (it may be presumed) contribute to mitigate the virulence, and prevent the diffusion of contagious diſtempers.

It has been formerly observed that the diſtrict of the town adjoining to the meadows was moſt liable to the prevalence of intermittent, or malignant fevers. The present salubrity of this situation may be juſtly attributed to the cultivation and draining of the ground, the considerable increase in the depth of the rivulet *Poe*, which flows through the whole extent of the vale; and to other modern agricultural improvements, preventing any accumulation of putrid vegetable matter.

Notwithſtanding the population of the town has been lately very much increased, by the extension and improvement of the collieries, public works and lime quarries, and the great encouragement given to various manufactories, and foundries; yet the general health of the people was never more perfect than it is at the present period: and when we compare the state of this situation with that of the neighbourhood, for the last three years, it will have appeared to have suffered much less sensibly from the fatal influence of Epidemic Contagions.

Other contemporary accounts paint a different picture. *The Town Book*, a record of the Manorial Court of St. Bees from 1702–1782, describes many infringements of town laws that would have been dangerous to public health. These include pavements in poor condition, cellars dug in dangerous situations, subsidence from mining, heaps of dung left in the streets to decay, and domestic animals roaming the streets. Animals were slaughtered and butchered alongside the Pow Beck, and children used the streets as privies. The *Cumberland Pacquet* newspaper of the time reports on the 'swine' that pollute the streets of the town and harass the inhabitants. Men worked in dangerous places in the mines and on the ships. Accidents were common. Children were frequently burnt or scalded from fires in cramped housing. What Joshua Dixon refers to as 'the lower class of people' lived a meagre existence in which hunger, exposure to the elements and disease were the norm. Central Whitehaven was a dangerous place to live and work.

The average life expectancy of the Whitehaven working man and his family at this time was no more than forty years. One third of all babies died before the age of one year. The staple diet was bread, barley, oats and potatoes with tea, skimmed milk, beer and fatty bacon. Overcrowding and poor sanitation, coupled with low resistance to infection, made the working population vulnerable to the regular epidemics of smallpox, typhus, enteric fevers, dysentery and tuberculosis. In 1791, Joshua Dixon made possibly the first ever observation on inequalities in health between the rich and the poor:

The acute Diseases of the Poor are unavoidably numerous and their chronic Infirmities frequently occur at an early Period of Life. Peculiarity of *Employment*, Improper *Food, Intemperance,* Inattention to *Cleanliness* and clear Ventilation; but especially incessant and extreme *Labour* during every Vicissitude in Weather or Season, expose them to the violent Attacks of various Disorders, from which those happily placed in a superior Station appear to be, in all Respects, totally exempt. With many, the natural Vigour and Energy of the System are so gradually impaired, and debilitated, as to finally render them obnoxious to the most distressful Maladies; or at least to have the Imbecilities of Old Age rapidly accelerated.

In 1817, a pestilential fever affected the lower part of the town with serious consequences. The appalling circumstances of the abodes of the poor described by Dixon, is typical of Whitehaven at that time.

Almost every person occupying the numerous, confined, filthy, and gloomy abodes of *Peter Court* and *Charles Street*, severely experienced this contagion. The miserable condition of many of these objects was exquisitely afflicting: their bed was of straw upon a damp earth floor. In several places, we found two or three patients sleeping together. The circumstances surrounding one singular and interesting case were exceedingly distressful. In a low room, almost immediately exposed to the open air, lay a father, three sons, and two daughters, at the head and foot of the same bed, with the slightest decayed coverlet. The man died, and the corpse was removed from his surrounding family. Can we conceive an occurrence more poignantly distressful, yet of which the sufferers, absorbed in their own painful feelings, were totally insensible? A similar equally, or perhaps more deplorable case, however, occurred soon after. A very infirm, middle-aged man died in the night, and, with great difficulty, in the morning, his arms were separated from the body of a son, which they closely enfolded. He was sleeping with his wife and four children: to a fifth the disease had been mortal a few days before. He made no complaint, suffered scarcely any confinement, nor solicited medical attention, though his family were under the care of the Dispensary. The effects of extreme poverty, especially that afflicting depression of mind, which always accompanies it, combining with the malignancy of contagion, might have hastened that fatal event, which occurred so early as on the second day. The numbers admitted upon our Register, in that situation, amount to 64; three were fatal cases. We attest, with great satisfaction, that in the decent houses adjoining to this seat of most *pestiferous contagion*, not the least appearance of it could be detected. The inhabitants, precluding, as far as possible, every communication with infected persons and places, were strictly attentive to the regular employment of *ablution, cleanliness,* and *ventilation*. To the Blessings which accompanied these prudent and judicious measures they are indebted for their past, present, and future prospect of freedom from disease.

WILLIAM BROWNRIGG M.D.F.R.S. *The doyen of Whitehaven Physicians 1712-1800.*
Artist Unknown. Courtesy of North Cumbria University Hospitals NHS Trust.

MEDICAL PRACTICE
IN LATE EIGHTEENTH-CENTURY
WHITEHAVEN

WHEN the Whitehaven Dispensary was founded in 1783, Whitehaven resembled the rest of England in having a diverse assortment of medical practitioners. Some were bona fide university educated practitioners holding medical degrees. Others had served local apprenticeships with a surgeon or an apothecary. In addition there was a smattering of irregular practitioners or 'quacks'. In the early years of the eighteenth century no system of formal education or medical registration existed, making it difficult to distinguish between the orthodox and the unqualified practitioner. Medical advice was obtained from a variety of sources including the clergy, or the well to do, some of whom pursued medicine as a hobby. Self-medication was very common. A network of midwives, wise women and nurses provided much of the medical input to the poor. Itinerant irregular practitioners travelled from town to town, advertising their curative skills and medicines on posters and billheads.

By the late eighteenth century, regular practitioners had evolved into the four specialities of Medicine, Surgery, Midwifery and Pharmacy. Physicians, practising Physic, had a university degree in Medicine, and were the pinnacle of the medical establishment. Their training also included principles of surgery and pharmacy, but they did not use this in practice. Instead, they devoted themselves to the diagnosis and treatment of illness by medical means. The Physician made a diagnosis by taking a comprehensive history of the illness, assessing the patient's habits and lifestyle, and observing any physical signs present. The pulse would be felt and described, often in fulsome terms, and the urine examined. The abdomen was palpated for tumours. Examination of the heart and lungs by percussion and auscultation, did not come into practice until the mid nineteenth century, when Laennec invented the stethoscope.

Surgery concentrated on the more obvious disorders of wounds, ulcers, fractures, dental disease and venereal disease. Some surgeons specialised in smallpox inoculation. Incisional surgery was a last resort as it was always painful and usually dangerous. Lithotomy for bladder stones, which were common, and amputations were the most frequent operations undertaken. The surgeons had evolved from the profession of Barber, by a system of apprenticeship, learning to pull teeth, set fractures and dress wounds. A Barber-Surgeon, Thomas Stephenson, practiced in Whitehaven in 1715. His apprentice John Cooke was also a Barber-Surgeon. The formation of the Company of Surgeons, in 1745, was an attempt to define the role and status of Surgeon more clearly and eventually led to the formation of the Royal College of Surgeons of London in 1800. In 1783, however, pure surgeons were few in number, comprising only 2.8 per cent of the registered medical practitioners in provincial England. The Register includes none in Cumberland. Although the officers of the Whitehaven Dispensary

AMPUTATION. *Five surgeons performing an amputation 1793.* Wellcome Library London.

included a surgeon from the outset, John Hamilton, who developed a great local reputation, we have no information on his medical background or qualifications.

The role of the traditional midwife also changed during the eighteenth century, particularly for the fee-paying classes. The traditional elderly female midwife was often seen as officious and meddling. A new profession of man-midwife made an appearance, with a university education, or a period of special study with an expert. These accoucheurs developed special skills in handling abnormal births, including the use of forceps. In London and the larger cities, their role extended into looking after normal pregnancies and deliveries. In Whitehaven at this time, pregnancy and labour came under the care of a network of family help, wise women and traditional midwives, with input from medical practitioners when needed. Midwifery cases form a significant part of the admissions to Whitehaven Dispensary.

The most numerous practitioners in provincial England in 1783 were the surgeon-apothecaries, comprising eighty-two per cent of the total. Sixty practiced in Cumbria, with three in Whitehaven. The origins of the Apothecary were with the Company of Grocers, until the Apothecaries Society was founded in 1615. Although apothecaries were part of the staff of the evolving voluntary hospitals and dispensaries, most plied their trade from their High Street shops. Their statutory duties were to dispense the prescriptions written by the Physicians. Naturally, the many patients unable to afford a Physician's fee would go to the apothecary in his shop for diagnosis and advice, as well as for his medications. Home visiting by the apothecary was common, especially if the local Physicians were too expensive, or unwilling to attend at anti-social times. By 1783, there were 2,607 surgeon-apothecaries in the provinces. As well as attending to patients visiting his shop, the surgeon-apothecary would make home visits, on foot or on horseback, leaving his shop in the care of his apprentice.

The place of the apothecary in the late eighteenth century was, in its turn, seriously challenged by the emergence of the druggist. Firmly based in a wholesale setting, druggists had become aware of the profits to be made from selling medicines to patients. Chemists had, originally, been exactly that, dealing in chemicals, to supply paints solvents and dyes to the building industry. Most kinds of tradesmen had sold drugs to the public, without the intervening aid of a medical opinion. Druggists evolved from the chemists and invested in shops displaying colourful bottles, pills, and potions. They also acquired the expertise to dispense the Physician's prescriptions. In the same way as the apothecaries had invaded the professional space of the Physicians, a century earlier, now the druggists, exploiting the frequent absences of the apothecary from his shop, became the main suppliers of medicines to the public.

While the tripartite division of medical practitioners into Physician, Surgeon, and Apothecary or Druggist was maintained in London and the larger cities, in smaller towns, such as Whitehaven, the distinction was often blurred. The Surgeon-Apothecary might offer a Physician's opinion, set fractures, dispense medicines, and advise on the management of a difficult labour. A list of licensed practitioners in eighteenth-century Whitehaven includes four Physicians, with four surgeons, three Surgeon-Apothecaries, one Druggist-Surgeon and seven Apothecaries.

Thomas Airey qualified as M.D. at Rheims, and practised in the town. He died in Jamaica in 1790. His son, Lancelot Airey proceeded M.D. at Leiden University in 1772. His thesis 'De Gonorrhoea Virulenta' was dedicated to his brother-in-law, the Revd Wilfrid Huddleston of St. Nicholas Church, a lifelong supporter and benefactor of the Whitehaven Dispensary. Richard Dixon obtained his M.D. at Leiden in 1739. His thesis 'De Phthisis Pulmonali' was a study of pulmonary tuberculosis. John Hamilton, the first surgeon appointed to the dispensary is listed as 'purveyor' as well as surgeon, while his namesake, Isaac Hamilton, is a surgeon-apothecary. Both men have surgeons and apothecaries as apprentices. Joseph Bragg, another surgeon-apothecary, finds a place as surgeon on the Dispensary medical committee. Joseph Harris, also a Dispensary surgeon, does not appear in the medical list of eighteenth-century Whitehaven, therefore his background and training are uncertain. Joseph Gunson, served as a surgeon in the English Army, before returning to practice in Whitehaven. Henry Crosthwaite obtained his doctorate from Leiden in 1789, with a thesis 'De Rachitide', dedicated to Joseph Stamper, a surgeon in nearby Workington. Crosthwaite was appointed to the Dispensary in 1792, with the title of Surgeon.

In the first half of the eighteenth century, it was common practice to travel to Europe to obtain a medical degree. Later, with the development of the London, and particularly, the Scottish hospitals, and the added difficulty of travel to Europe in time of war, British qualification became the norm. Of the 273 provincial English Physicians listed in the Medical Register of 1783, only thirty-four had qualified in Europe, and by then most were elderly or retired. It was possible to purchase an M.D. from St. Andrews, for example, for a fee of £30, and two favourable references. Almost half of the English provincial Physicians registered in 1783, had qualified in Edinburgh, including Joshua Dixon in 1768.

Even as late as 1815, a surgical career began with an apprenticeship. Joseph Robinson was a Surgeon-Apothecary in Whitehaven, who served on the Dispensary committee. In September 1815, he took on an apprentice, Thomas Mitchell. His Deed of Apprenticeship is dated October 17, 1815.

Thomas Mitchell doth place and bind himself Apprentice to the said Joseph Robinson to be taught and instructed in the Art, Trade, Mystery or Occupation of a Surgeon and Apothecary and to continue to serve him as an Apprentice from the 24th day of September past, for and unto the full End and Term of Five years.

During which all said term, the said Thomas Mitchell doth hereby covenant and promise that he shall and will well faithfully serve, demean himself, and be just and true to the said Joseph Robinson as his Master, and keep his Secrets, and everywhere readily obey all his lawful Commands. He shall not do any Hurt, Prejudice or Damage to the Estate, Goods, Effects and merchandise of his Master. He shall not play at Cards, Dice, or any unlawful Games, nor haunt, use or frequent Playhouses, Inns, Taverns or Alehouses, except about his Master's Business to be transacted there. He shall not contract Matrimony, nor at any time during the said Term, Day or Night, absent himself or depart from the Service of the said Master. And shall find and provide himself with good and sufficient meat, drinks, washing, lodging and clothing apparel.

Despite the apparently draconian nature of the contract, this particular apprentice appears to have survived! In 1821, the name of Mr. Thomas Mitchell sits proudly among the list of Surgeons appointed to the Dispensary.

WHITEHAVEN DISPENSARY

THE Dispensary movement of late eighteenth-century England arose from the same principles of medical philanthropy, which had resulted in the growth of the voluntary hospitals earlier in the century. The voluntary hospitals relied on charitable donations and provided inpatient care for the poor and needy. Westminster Hospital was the first to be established in 1720, followed by Guy's, St. George's and the Middlesex, in 1745. In the provinces, the earliest voluntary hospitals appeared in the south-east of the country, in Winchester, Bristol and Bath. In the north of England, hospitals in Liverpool, Newcastle and Manchester opened between 1749 and 1752. John Coakley Lettsom (1744–1815) is generally credited as the founding father of the dispensary movement, as he was instrumental in setting up the first dispensary in the capital, in Aldersgate Street, in 1770. Lettsom enjoyed a high reputation as a Physician in London. His philanthropy was based on his Quaker principles, and even when able to command high fees from his patients, he held free surgeries for the poor. He became an additional Physician to the Aldersgate dispensary in 1783. By that time, there were nine dispensaries operating in the capital and six in the provinces. Provincial dispensaries

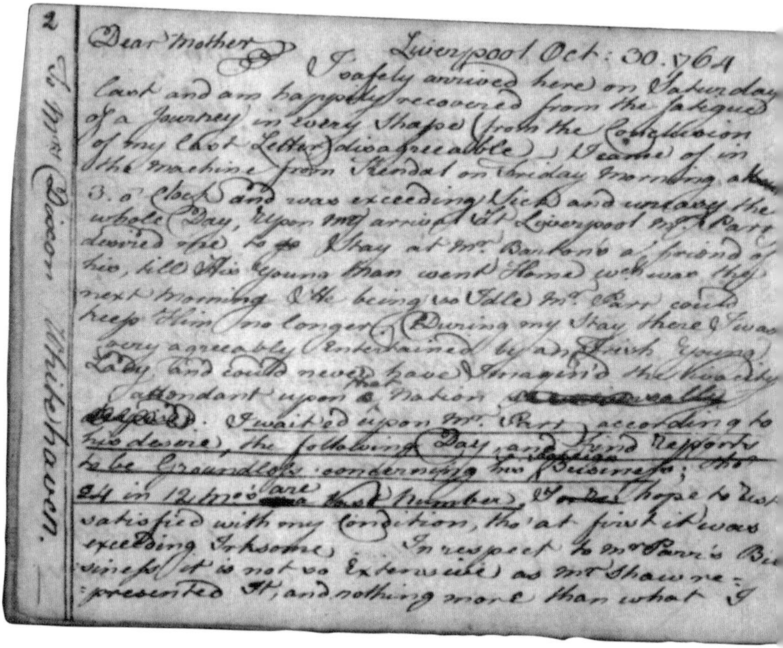

Handwritten letter (transcribed):

2

To Mrs Dicson Whitehaven

Dear Mother   Liverpool Oct: 30. 64

I safely arrived here on Saturday last and am happily recovered from the fatigue of a journey in every shape ... of my last letter disagreeable. I learned of in the machine from Kendal on Friday morning at 3 o'clock and was exceeding sick and uneasy the whole day, upon my arrival at Liverpool my ... desired us to Stay at Mr. Benton's a friend of his, till Mr. Young then went home (who was left) next morning. the being no Table Mr. Carr could keep them no longer. During my Stay there I was very agreeably entertained by an Irish young Lady and could never have imagined the kindly attendant upon a nation ... I waited upon Mr. Carr according to his desire, the following Day, and find Reports to be Groundless concerning his Business; the 24 in 12 mo's are the Number, I ... hope to be satisfied with my condition, tho' at first it was exceeding Irksome. In respect to Mr. Penn's Business it is not so Extensive as Mr. Shaw represented it, and nothing more than what I

---

originated in thriving towns and cities. Stroud has a claim to be the first provincial dispensary to open, possibly in 1774. The town had prospered because of the local wool trade. Newcastle-upon-Tyne and Liverpool dispensaries followed in 1778, and a successful dispensary opened in Carlisle in 1782.

Similar to the voluntary hospitals, dispensaries were financed by subscription. They were designed to provide medical care to the poor on an outpatient basis; sick patients were visited at home, usually by the Apothecary. Subscribers could, by 'letters of recommendation', refer appropriate cases for treatment at the dispensary. Medical staff held honorary unpaid appointments at the dispensaries, and depended for

LETTER FROM JOSHUA DIXON TO HIS MOTHER IN WHITEHAVEN, ANNOUNCING HIS SAFE ARRIVAL IN LIVERPOOL. *October 30th 1764.* Wellcome Library London.

their living on private practice. Only the apothecary, who usually resided at the dispensary, was paid an annual salary. His duties, outlined in the History and Statutes of the Newcastle Dispensary, (1790) would be typical of the post:

> The apothecary shall reside conſtantly at the dispensary, to receive the letters of recommendation, and transmit them to the Physicians or surgeons; to keep a regiſter of the patients; and to draw up monthly and annual returns of the sick…He shall be empowered in slight casualties, to give relief to patients without delay, and to receive them without recommendations. He, with the assiſtance of the apprentices, is to compound and dispense the prescriptions of the Physicians; affixing to each medicine the patient's name and the manner of using it. He is to visit home patients in acute and dangerous diseases once a day, or oftener,

and those in chronic and dangerous diseases twice a week; and may prescribe in urgent cases in the absence of the Physician…. He is to present a book to each Physician, on his attending day at the Dispensary, containing a list of the outpatients and home patients in his respective district.

Patients attending the dispensary were referred to as 'admissions'. This term referred to an admission to the charity and not an admission to hospital, as we understand it today. Most of the dispensaries were small and did not have facilities for inpatient care.

A Dispensary for Whitehaven had been suggested as early as 1776. The *Cumberland Pacquet* reported on July 11, 1776, that, 'Small Pox appeared in Whitehaven last week and has since spread with most surprising rapidity'. This prompted Sir James Lowther to call for some provision of free medical care for the poor of the town. Instrumental in setting up the Dispensary was Dr. Joshua Dixon. Born in 1744, Dixon was the son of a Whitehaven mariner. In 1764, he travelled to Liverpool where he served as assistant to Edward Parr, an Apothecary and merchant with interests in the slave trade. His salary as an Apothecary's assistant was thirty shillings a year. Dixon's duties included pulling teeth and bleeding his master's patients, as well as preparing and dispensing medicines. He studied medicine at Edinburgh University, where he qualified M.D. in 1768. He returned to Whitehaven to practice as a Physician at 7 Lowther Street. On June 9, 1775, Joshua Dixon married Anne Heather in St. James Church, Whitehaven. They had six children, three of whom died in infancy.

An editorial appeared in the *Cumberland Pacquet* on February 11, 1783:

We have the pleasure of announcing to the public the commencement of a very necessary and laudable institution in this place, viz. that of a DISPENSARY, for supplying the SICK POOR with ADVICE and MEDICINES GRATIS. For this purpose, Sir James Lowther, Bart., has given a benefaction of ONE HUNDRED POUNDS, and it is hoped his example will be followed by other gentlemen, either by benefactions, or annual subscriptions, in so ample a manner, as to make this establishment answer all the benevolent ends for which it is designed. (See the advertisement) The following are the outlines of the plan:

A small house containing two or three rooms is to be engaged: one of these is to be appropriated to the business of the apothecary, and furnished with medicines; and the other two for the admission and examination of patients. The officers of the Dispensary are a President, Committee, Treasurer, Physician, Surgeon and Apothecary. The last only to receive a gratuity for his labour. Certain hours of attendance are to be fixed upon, and the sick, who are not able to appear at the Dispensary, are to be visited at least once a day in their respective habitations. The requisites for admission to be the poverty of the person, and a recommendation of the clergy, magistrates or subscribers. A list of the Dispensary patients, their diseases and events, will be annually published, with a view to determine the utility of the institution, which must of course, receive the support of all well disposed persons, whose circumstances will admit of their contributing to it.

The same issue contained the following advertisement:

WHITEHAVEN DISPENSARY.

THIS institution is designed for supplying the SICK POOR of the town of Whitehaven with Advice and Medicines gratis. Proposals for establishing this most necessary Charity may be seen at the Coffee Rooms, where BENEFACTIONS and SUBSCRIPTIONS will be acceptable.

Books are open for Subscriptions at Mr. Buckham's Coffee Rooms, Mr. Haile's The King's Arms, Mr. Fisher's The Golden Lion, Mrs. Atkin's The King's Arms, Mrs. Nicholson's The Indian King, Mr. Walton's The Black Lion and at Ware's Printing Office.

We are extremely happy to observe that, since our last,

there have been several handsome subscriptions added to the DISPENSARY for the relief of the sick poor in this town. All objections being removed by the regulations annexed to the Subscriptions book at Mr. Buckham's coffee rooms, there can be no doubt of sufficient contributions being obtained to carry this useful plan into execution. Those who are induced through the noblest motive, that of HUMANITY, are requested to peruse these regulations and any hints, which can be suggested for their improvement, will be adopted. As the intention of the charity is to diffuse as much public good as possible, the proposers are desirous of using every means that can the most speedily effect it.

The Cumberland Pacquet   March 11, 1783

"DOCTOR JOSHUA DIXON, the proposer of a Medical Dispensary at Whitehaven, presents his most respectful acknowledgments to those gentlemen who have generously endeavoured to promote its establishment. With a view to repay a few of the many obligations Doctor Dixon has received from this country, and gratify at the same time the most acceptable sensations of humanity, was this institution recommended to the approbation of the opulent; and nowhere could its expediency be more apparent than in a large commercial town, not advantaged by any similar charity, especially at a season when infectious fever very generally and potently prevails. Most sincere are his wishes that these considerations may be permitted to excite the liberality of the public. In the meantime, the present state of the dispensary subscriptions appearing inadequate to the purpose of carrying its object into immediate and effective execution, Doctor Dixon, solely actuated by principles of gratitude and benevolence, will afford himself the exalted satisfaction of continuing to provide the sick poor with every requisite medical attendance he can conveniently prepare or procure for them."

The Cumberland Pacquet   March 18, 1783

"Objections towards a DISPENSARY in this town now being happily removed, and such regulations framed as cannot fail of meeting the approbation of the public, there is a fair prospect of this charity being soon instituted."

JOHN HAMILTON, SURGEON
EXTRAORDINARY, WHITEHAVEN
DISPENSARY 1739 – 1814.
*Image in Daniel Hay, Illustrated History
of Whitehaven.* Courtesy of Michael Moon.

The Cumberland Pacquet   April 29, 1783

"Friday laſt, a meeting was held at Buckham's coffee house of
the subscribers to the Medical DISPENSARY in this town, when
Mr. Robinson was elected Apothecary to the Charity. The other
officers were also fixed. The particulars will appear in our next."

The Cumberland Pacquet   6 May, 1783

"We hear a commodious house in Scotch -Street, near Duke-
Street is taken and fitting up for the DISPENSARY. The following
are the Officers of the Charity, chosen at the laſt meeting.

President   Sir James Lowther, Bart.:–   **Vice-Presidents**
Anthony Benn Esq., The Rev. Mr. Huddlestone:– **Treasurer** Mr.
John Gibson:– **Secretary** Mr. P.H. Younger:– **Physician** Joshua
Dixon M.D.:– **Surgeon** Mr. John Hamilton:– **Apothecary** Mr.
William Robinson with a salary of £30 per annum.

Monthly Committee Messrs. Isaac Littledale, George Stalker, Samuel Potter, John Barns, Henry Fletcher, Richard Fletcher, John Bateman.

Medical Committee Dr. Joshua Dixon, Messrs.John Hamilton, John Peele, Joseph Harris, Joseph Bragg, Surgeons. Mark Wylie, Druggist

In order to render the Charity as extensively useful as its nature will admit, it has been resolved that that Subscribers in the country shall have the right of recommending patients within 10 miles of Whitehaven."

The Whitehaven Dispensary opened on June 30, 1783, not, as generally believed, at 107 Queen Street, but in 'a commodious house in Scotch-street, near Duke-Street.' It was one of the earliest of the English provincial dispensaries.

A GENERAL STATE

OF THE

WHITEHAVEN DISPENSARY

FOR THE YEAR 1783

In recommending this charitable institution to the patronage of the opulent, a variety of arguments, founded on the principles of Christian benevolence, and the feelings of humanity were necessarily employed: the testimony of experience has since been obtained, decisively to prove its utility. The great numbers of miserable objects, labouring under the complicated evils of Poverty and Pain, who have been either entirely cured, or considerably relieved of their complaints, proclaim it's truest praise: and at the same time, suggest the most persuasive motives to animate all who are blessed with the ability, to feed and replenish the fountain, from which these salutary streams diffusively flow. To the lowest class of laborious, infirm and aged people, who solely and with difficulty, acquire the frugal necessities of life, the aids of Medicine and Surgery are also liberally dispensed. They have now an asylum from all those calamities to which sickness, in their contracted

N.B. This chapter is Joshua Dixon's Annual Report for 1783.

circumstances, renders them exceedingly liable. The past season, from it's remarkable and permanent severity, has very much increased the number of applications to this charity; the benevolent establishment of which, may indulge the grateful satisfaction of having perfectly obviated not a few of those distresses, to which the indigent and industrious were consequently exposed.

The principal registered diseases will properly suggest a few brief observations. With regard to their nature and tendency, more minute information may be received at the Dispensary, where the cases and their modes of treatment are particularised, and the whole, with their respective events, systematically arranged.

The first objects of this charity were those who had laboured under the various and poignant sufferings of long protracted disease, the symptoms of which could only admit a temporary mitigation. In the autumnal months of September, October and November, a nervous fever, distinguished by very powerful characters took place in Charles Street., extending its malignancy to the adjacent soft confined situations. To the usual medical attentions was added an especial regard to the regimen of the patients, cleanliness and pure air being strictly enjoined, and every precaution taken to prevent the communication of disease. The necessitous sick were also supplied with requisite quantities of wine, and occasionally recommended to public and private charities. Twenty-six of these cases were then admitted, and happily they all recovered. During the winter, a numerous strain of pectoral and inflammatory disorders (to which this climate and season are particularly liable) very urgently obtained, especially catarrhs, consumptions with more acute rheumatic and pleuritic affections. In the beginning of October, the small pox became epidemical, and has continued for these last eight months. Of the patients who suffered the natural infection (in all three hundred and twenty) seventy three died and sixty nine with difficulty recovered from a ſtate of remarkable confluence and danger. The Hooping cough has lately very mildly and partially prevailed, requiring for the moſt part scarce any medical assiſtance. To the influence of this salutary season will the cure of the present and prevention of future disease be chiefly remitted. The only other contagion of any moment was dysentery, which has at different periods of the preceding year, repeatedly and violently occurred. In the contracted habitations of the indigent, where many of the essential necessities, and all the conveniences of life were frequently wanting, it's baneful progress and effects became not less extensive than potent. Forty-nine of these patients have already been admitted; thirty-one were dismissed cured, and the remaining eighteen ſtill continue upon the Books. Relative to the surgical cases, in which the aids of art were more obviously and certainly useful, upwards of two hundred persons have experienced the benefits of this inſtitution.

The influence of this charity since its eſtablishment, has been gradually and considerably extended. Regardful of our maritime situation, and the dangers to which we are inevitably exposed, it was deemed eligible to form a connection with the LONDON HUMANE SOCIETY, and very generally, to diſtribute its judicious inſtructions, procuring at the same time a complete apparatus for the recovery of persons apparently drowned. The modes of treatment beſt adapted to reſtore such deplorable objects will now be universally known, and the intelligent of every profession are earneſtly requeſted occasionally put them in immediate and vigorous execution.

The practice of general inoculation was next very ſtrenuously recommended, and the advances deducible from it publicly announced. The poor were, however so remarkably averse to the proposal, that thirty children could only be permitted to comply with it, not an individual of which required the leaſt medical attention.

Several additional subscriptions and augmentations for the ensuing year have already been received, and it is ardently hoped that the more general contributions of the public will afford the pleasing opportunity of perfeᶜtly accomplishing the benevolent intentions of this charity.

An ACCOUNT *of the* PATIENTS *admitted, from* June 30, 1783, *to* June 14, 1784

Recommended and regiſtered	–	–	–	1467
Trivial caſes	–	–	–	–	433
Children prepared for the ſmall-pox		–	–	157
				2057

The STATE *of the* REGISTER

Cured	–	–	–	–	–	1089
Relieved	–	–	–	–	–	36
Incurable	–	–	–	–	–	7
Irregular	–	–	–	–	–	5
Dead *	–	–	–	–	–	110
Remaining upon the books		–	–	–	220
						1467

Of the above, 1021 were attended at their own habitations.

* Many of theſe patients became the viᶜtims of chronic affeᶜtions and ſeventy-three ſuffered a very confluent ſpecies of ſmall pox.

D I S E A S E S.

Intermittent fever –	9
Inflammatory fever –	55
Nervous fever – –	27
Hectic fever – –	4
Worm fever – –	84
External Inflammation	25
Inflammation of the eyes	27
Inflammation of the brain	1
Inflammation of the forethroat	12
Inflammation of the lungs	51
Inflammation of the Bowels	1
Acute Rheumatism –	16
Chronic Rheumatism	29
Eryfipelas – –	8
Inflammatory eruptions	15
Natural Small pox –	320
Inoculated Small pox	30
Miliary fever – –	2
Haemorrhages – –	17
Confumption – –	37
Abortion – –	1
Catarrh – –	35
Catarrh of old age – –	7
Dyfentery – –	49
Headache and vertigo – –	32
Palfy – –	6
Fainting – –	3
Stomach complaints – –	46
Flatulency – –	42
Carried forward	991

Brought over	991
Convulfions – –	4
Epilepfy – –	9
Afthma – –	29
Hooping cough –	24
Colic – –	47
Diarrhœa – –	25
Hyfteria – –	4
Melancholy – –	2
Chronic weaknefs –	22
Dropfy – –	15
Rickets – –	5
Scrophula – –	20
Lues venerea – –	7
Jaundice – –	4
Dimnefs of fight – –	8
Deafnefs – –	2
Gravel – –	13
Aneurifm – –	1
Schirrus – –	2
Cancer – –	4
Rupture – –	2
Scald head – –	9
White fwelling –	2
Scorbutic eruptions	98
Luxations, fractures, & fprains	18
Ulcers and abfcefses	42
Contufions wounds & Burns	58
Total	1467

BENEFACTORS.

	£.	s.	d.
The Right Hon. the			
Earl of Lonſdale	100	0	0
George Bigland Eſq.	10	0	0
	110	0	0

SUBSCRIBERS.
A

James Atkinſon	0	10	6
William Alexander	0	5	0
Benjamin Antrobus	0	5	0

B

William Brownrigg M.D.			
F.R.S	2	2	0
Anthony Benn, Eſq.			
Henſingham	2	2	0
John Barns	1	1	0
John Bateman	1	1	0
John Beck	1	1	0
Joſeph Bragg	1	1	0
Henry Barnes	0	10	6
Iſaac Barras and Co.	0	10	6
Robert Blakeney	0	10	6
Wilfrid Blaiklin	0	10	6
Henry Bragg	0	10	6
Darcy Bowen	0	10	6
John Bowneſs	0	10	6
Carried forward	£. 13	2	0

	£.		
Brought over	£. 13	2	0
John Bragg	0	5	0
Iſaac Bragg	0	5	0

C

John Chriſtian Eſq.			
Workington Hall	5	5	0
Rev. C.C.Church	1	1	0
Rev. John Colquhoun	1	1	0
Walter Chambre	0	10	6
Robert Carter	0	5	0
James Corkhill	0	2	6
Hugh Corkhill	0	2	6

D

John Dixon Eſq.	2	2	0
J.L. Deſvillers	1	1	0
Joſhua Dixon M.D.	1	1	0
Peter Dixon	1	1	0
John Douglas	0	10	6
John Dawſon	0	10	6
John Dunn	0	5	0

F

L.W. Fl;etcher Eſq.			
Hutton Hall	2	2	0
Robert Fiſher	1	11	6
R Fletcher, Merchant	1	11	6
H. Fletcher ditto	1	11	6
Robert Ferguſon	1	1	0
Thomas Fiſher	1	1	0
R. Fletcher, Mercer	1	1	0
Henry Fletcher	0	10	6
Carried forward	£. 39	0	6

	£.		
Brought over	39	o	6
Mrs. Jane Fletcher	o 10		6
Steven Farifh	o	5	o
Mrs. Barbara Fletcher	o	5	o

G

Peter Gale	1	1	o
John Gibbon	1	1	o
Benjamin Gilliat	o 10		6
Mrs. Greybourne	o	5	o

H

Rev. Wilfrid Hudlefton	2	2	o
Jofeph Hofkins Efq.	2	2	o
John Hodgfon	2	2	o
John Hartley Efq.	1	1	o
Thomas Hartley Efq.	1	1	o
John Hamilton, Surgeon	1	1	o
Jofeph Harris ditto	1	1	o
P.J.Heywood Efq.	1	1	o
James Hogarth	1	1	o
George Hall	o 10		6
Thomas Harrifon	o 10		6
William Harrifon	o 10		6
Thomas Horne	o 10		6
James Hall	o	5	o
John Huddlefton	o	5	o

J

Edward and John Johnfton	1	1	o
W. Jackfon, Kefwick	1	1	o

K

Rev. James Kirkpatrick	1	1	o
Thomas Kirkpatrick	o	5	o

	£.		
Carried forward	61	10	6

	£.		
Brought over	61	10	6
Robert Key	o	5	o
Mifs Kelfick	o	5	o

L

Ifaac Littledale	2	2	o
Henry Littledale	2	2	o
Thomas Lutwidge Efq.	1	1	o
John Lancafter	o 10		6
James Lowes	o 10		6

M

Robert Miller	o 10		6
George Miller	o 10		6
John Mcbride	o	5	o
John Moore	o	5	o

N

Rev. Henry Nicholfon	1	1	o

P

Samuel Potter	1 11		6
John Parker	1	1	o
John Peele, Surgeon	1	1	o
John Piper	1	1	o
Peter Pearfon	1	1	o
Jofeph Piper	1	1	o
William Penn	o	5	o
William Philipfon	o	5	o
John Pirie	o	5	o

R

Chriftopher Robinfon	o 10		6
John Rumney	o 10		6
John Richardfon	o	5	o
John Roblon	o	3	o

	£.		
Carried forward	78	18	o

Brought over	£. 78	18	0	

S

Joseph Senhouse Esq.	2	2	0
Alexander Spittal	1	1	0
George Stalker	1	1	0
Rev. James Sedgwick	0	10	6
Robert Sanderson	0	10	6
Miss Senhouse	0	10	6
John Shepherd	0	2	6
John Storey	0	2	6

T

John Tate	1	1	0
Francis Telfair	0	5	0
John Thompson	0	5	0

U

George Vickers	0	10	6
Oliver Ufsinfon	0	2	6

W

R. Wordsworth Esq.	1	1	0
John Walker	1	1	0
John Wilson	1	1	0
Mark Wylie	1	1	0
Mrs. Wybergh	1	1	0
J. Ware and Son	1	1	0
Joseph Wilson	0	10	6
John White	0	5	0
Nathaniel Wilson	0	5	0
James Witherington	0	5	0

Y

Peter How Younger	1	1	0

Total Subscriptions	£. 95	15	0
Total Benefactions	£. 110	10	0
	£. 206	5	0

DISBURSEMENTS

Drugs and medicines	34	3	8
Fixtures and furniture	13	7	0
Printing and stationaries	7	9	0
Joiners and Painters work }	5	18	4
Coal, candles, wine, phials, and sundry small articles }	11	9	6
House rent	7	10	0
Apothecary's salary	30	0	0
Pocket instruments	3	1	6
	£. 112	19	0

Total Benefactions	110	10	0
Subscriptions	95	15	0
	£. 206	5	0
Disbursements	112	19	0
Balance in Treafurer's Hands }	£. 93	6	0

BENEFACTIONS and SUBSCRIPTIONS.
A Short ABSTRACT *from the* RULES

The peculiar objects of the charity are the sick and lame poor, who can derive no benefit from any similar institution. Domestic servants and apprentices must by no means become dispensary patients.

The persons coming accurately under the above description are to be admitted by a letter of recommendation, signed by a subscriber, and addressed to the medical officers of the Dispensary. In case, however, of accidents, or very urgent affections, where delay may be attended with very dangerous consequences, proper objects will receive assistance , upon application, without a letter of recommendation.

That proper objects, when affected with trivial disease, receive the benefits of this charity without any recommendation.

That governers and qualified subscribers be intitled to recommend an unlimited number of patients suffering epidemical diseases.

That the governors and qualified subscribers be intitled to recommend a double number of patients to the benefits of this charity.

That the sick poor residing in the country, are only to be recommended by the governors and qualified subscribers of their respective parishes.

THE SCOURGE
OF
SMALLPOX

During the first year of the Dispensary, from June 1783 until June 1784, 1,467 patients were seen by letter of recommendation from a subscriber to the Dispensary. In addition, 433 patients presented themselves to the Dispensary without any recommendation. These were classed as 'trivial cases' and seen by the apothecary. Trivial cases would be minor injuries or illness, which did not require the attentions of the Physician or Surgeon. They do not appear in the list of diseases seen. As many as 1,021 of the recommended cases were visited 'in their own habitations' by the apothecary, William Robinson. At the first anniversary meeting of the Dispensary, on June 14, 1784, 'it was agreed to present the Apothecary, with five guineas, as a gratuity, for his close attention to the duties of his office, and in consideration of his having visited, as long as was necessary, so large a number as 1,021 patients in their own habitations.' This means that only 466 of the patients recommended were actually seen at the dispensary during the course of the year. The mortality of dispensary patients in that first year was unusually high, with 110 deaths. Seventy-three of these deaths were from smallpox.

Smallpox was the most feared disease in eighteenth-century Whitehaven, because of its highly infectious nature, and a mortality rate of around twenty per cent. The disease originated in subtropical central Africa, and reached Western Europe, in the early Middle Ages. In the early seventeenth century, annual bills of mortality began to be published in London, and these make it clear that smallpox had replaced the plague as the major contagious threat in the city. Smallpox was endemic in London at this time, increasing in some years to epidemic proportions, when it was responsible for up to thirty per cent of all deaths. Epidemics were recorded throughout the seventeenth and early eighteenth centuries with a periodicity of two to four years. An isolated community, such as Whitehaven, would suffer smallpox only when it was introduced from outside. Whitehaven was particularly vulnerable in this respect, because its maritime development had resulted in increasing trade links with Liverpool, Dublin and the Isle of Man, where smallpox was usually endemic. The transatlantic trade

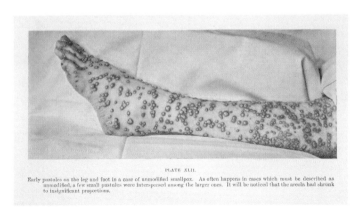

PLATE XLII.

Early pustules on the leg and foot in a case of unmodified smallpox. As often happens in cases which must be described as unmodified, a few small pustules were interspersed among the larger ones. It will be noticed that the areola had shrunk to insignificant proportions.

EARLY PUSTULES OF SMALLPOX. Wellcome Library London.

did not introduce smallpox into the town, as, if smallpox occurred in a ship departing America for Whitehaven, the sufferers would have either died or recovered well before the end of the voyage. The smallpox threat came from closer to home.

Smallpox is due to a poxvirus and is spread by droplet infection. The two-week incubation period is followed by fever, malaise, aching limbs and, on the second to the fourth day by a rash. The rash begins as fluid filled blisters (vesicles), which then fill with pus (pustules) before scabbing over. The nature of the rash is the clue to the severity and likely outcome of the illness. Dixon recognised the observation that the more numerous and confluent the skin lesions, the worse the prognosis. Smallpox was classified on this basis as discrete, with a good outlook; confluent, with a poor outlook, and haemorrhagic, where bleeding into the skin heralded a fatal conclusion. Secondary infection and septicaemia were responsible for most deaths and survivors of major attacks ended up with severe disfigurements or 'pock marks' on the skin. Blindness was common. Treatment was ineffective and controversial. Traditional treatment was the 'hot method', in which sweating and purging were used to produce heat and assist nature in ridding the body of the presumed noxious agent. Sydenham, the 'English Hippocrates', introduced the 'cold method' in which a regime of light covering, fresh air and cool drinks evoked the opposite effect. Many sufferers relied on 'quacks' and folk remedies.

It was from the realms of folk remedies that inoculation against smallpox evolved. It had long been practice in rural communities, to allow exposure of susceptible children to mild cases of smallpox, in the hope that they too would acquire a mild variety of the disease. Professor Munro, of Edinburgh, in 1765, confirmed that in the Scottish Highlands, it was common practice to infect children by rubbing them with a 'kindly pock'. In Wales, a widespread folk custom was to 'buy the smallpox' by sending children to a house where a mild case of smallpox was recovering, with pennies to buy token goods. Sometimes buying the pox occurred literally, with scabs of smallpox, or strands of cloth soaked in the fluid from pox vesicles, being exchanged for money, and used to infect healthy children.

A more formal procedure of inoculation was practised in and around Constantinople in the early decades of the eighteenth century, and observed by several of the Europeans living there. The practice may have originated in Greece, or Georgia. A Greek woman from the suburbs of Constantinople is said to have inoculated 4,000 persons during the smallpox epidemic there in 1706. Fluid smallpox matter was taken from the pustules of a mild case of smallpox with discrete skin lesions. The matter was placed in a warmed stopped vial and conveyed to the place of inoculation. A few punctures were made with a surgeon's needle in the skin of the upper arm of the recipient, until blood came. A drop of the fluid matter of the smallpox was mixed with the blood and the site then covered by a walnut shell. Several sites were inoculated. The outcome of inoculation varied. Sometimes a single pustule appeared at the site of inoculation. Others developed a mild illness with few discrete skin lesions, but some did experience clinical smallpox, and there were fatalities. Such cases were, of course, infectious in the natural way and, unless quarantined, could infect their susceptible contacts. What became clear, however, was that those who had been inoculated in this way, were no longer susceptible to infection by the natural smallpox.

Lady Mary Wortley Montague is credited with pioneering the use of the new inoculation in England, and introducing it to her circle of friends in the Royal Family. Lady Mary was the wife of the English ambassador in Constantinople, and had observed the practice at first hand. In the spring of 1718, she had her five-year-old son inoculated by a Greek

LADY MARY WORTLEY MONTAGUE. *Oil Portrait after Zincke.* Wellcome Library London.

woman, under the direction of Charles Maitland, a Scottish surgeon attached to the Embassy. Lady Mary returned to London in 1718. In 1719, a smallpox epidemic caused 3,229 deaths in the city, and in 1721, a smaller epidemic caused several deaths in her family and social circle. Lady Mary resolved to have her three-year-old daughter Mary inoculated, and sent for Charles Maitland, who was initially reluctant to be involved in such a high profile procedure.

Maitland did eventually obtain some suitable smallpox matter and inoculated the girl on both arms. Three members of the Royal College of Physicians observed the course of the illness, which emerged on the tenth night with fever and a mild smallpox rash. In a few days, she had recovered. The Montagu case aroused interest in inoculation in professional circles, and in the Royal Family.

Lady Mary was a close friend of the Princess of Wales, who had been worried by the grave illness of her eldest daughter Anne, initially thought to be smallpox, but later reconsidered to be measles. Nevertheless, the Princess decided to have her two younger daughters inoculated against smallpox, but not before acquiring further evidence of the safety of the procedure. King George the first was petitioned to pardon six criminals under sentence of death, in Newgate prison, provided they agreed to an experiment in which they would be subjected to inoculation against smallpox. On July 24, 1721, several Physicians and Surgeons from the Royal household visited Newgate prison to select suitable prisoners for inoculation and to 'prepare' them for the procedure. Preparation involved purging, blood letting or the use of tonics, all designed to prime the system to a receptive state. Charles Maitland was the chosen inoculator and the operation was performed on three male and three female prisoners on the morning of August 9, 1721. Several eminent Physicians, including the royal Physician, Sir Hans Sloan, supervised the procedure. Maitland repeated the inoculation on five of the prisoners on August 12, fearing the original material had been ineffective. Five prisoners developed a mild form of smallpox and recovered. One man had no reaction to the inoculation. It later transpired he had already suffered the natural smallpox. The success of inoculation in preventing infection by natural smallpox was tested by sending one of the prisoners, a girl of nineteen, to care for the smallpox victims of an epidemic in Hertford.

Maitland supervised her exposure to confluent smallpox over a period of six weeks. She remained free of the disease.

In due course, on April 17,1722, the Prince and Princess of Wales had their daughters, Princess Amelia aged eleven, and Princess Caroline aged nine, inoculated by the King's surgeon, with the ubiquitous Charles Maitland supplying the smallpox matter and directing the places of incision. The Royal equanimity was seriously disturbed four days after the procedure, by the death from smallpox of the young son of the Earl of Sunderland, who had been inoculated two weeks earlier. The Princesses, however, endured a mild illness and recovered in two weeks. Not so lucky was the nineteen-year-old footman of Lord Bathhurst, who had been inoculated at the same time, and died two weeks later. The subsequent lull in inoculations gave impetus to opponents of the very concept of introducing foreign pathological matter into healthy recipients.

The controversy that followed was less of a scientific discussion than a posturing of deeply held views. Prominent among opponents of the practice of Inoculation, was the Revd. Mr. Edward Massey, of St. Andrew's Holborn, who preached on the 'Dangerous and Sinful Practice of Inoculation'. There were opponents also in the Royal College of Physicians and in the Royal Society. Dr. William Wagstaffe, Physician to St. Bartholomew's Hospital produced a paper entitled, 'Shewing the Danger and Uncertainty of Inoculating the Smallpox'. The situation was clarified by the work of Dr. James Jurin, a Cambridge medical graduate and a fellow of the Royal Society, under the Presidency of Sir Isaac Newton. Jurin gathered together such statistics as were available and showed that the risk of death overall from the natural smallpox was about one in eight cases, rising to one in five in severe epidemics. The risk of death from inoculated smallpox in England was only one in ninety. Data collected prospectively by Jurin between1721 and 1727 confirmed these figures. The great smallpox epidemic in London in 1746, gave further impetus to the practice of Inoculation and led to the establishment of the Smallpox and Inoculation Hospital in the capital. Inoculation until then had been largely practiced in the affluent classes. This was the first attempt to bring the benefits of Inoculation to the poor.

Joshua Dixon was a committed proponent of inoculation, probably due to his experiences as an apprentice in Liverpool. In his first Annual Report, Dixon bemoans that the 'poor are so remarkable averse to the proposal,' that, despite the presence of smallpox in the town, he could persuade only thirty children to be inoculated. Two years later, numbers inoculated had risen to 206. There was considerable antagonism to Inoculation in the town. Dixon includes in his casebook 'Children prepared for the smallpox'. This refers to the practice of admitting the child to the Dispensary and preparing the system for inoculation, by bleeding, purging or cooling in order to achieve an optimum state for inoculation. Of course such 'prepared' children would be still be susceptible to natural smallpox, until they received the inoculation. This caused confusion and fuelled opposition in Whitehaven to this innovation. Dixon had to work hard to convince the sceptics.

The first general meeting of the Whitehaven Dispensary, following its opening, had been held on December 1,1783. By this date 423 patients had been admitted to the Dispensary, of whom 277 had been cured and only sixteen had died. There were 110 patients still on the books. Thirty-four children had been 'prepared for the smallpox', and a further twenty-eight were inoculated. Some townsfolk supposed that children 'prepared for the smallpox' were somehow more liable to catch the natural disease with fatal results, and were vocal opponents of Inoculation. Dixon was forced to clarify his figures in the *Cumberland Pacquet*:

> The State of the Dispensary in this town having been grossly misunderstood by some, we think it not improper to lay it again before our readers. Our reason for repeating this is that we have been informed some supposed that 16 of the smallpox patients had died; though the truth is that they all got well through the disorder, without requiring any attendance from the professional officers of the Dispensary.

Dixon is referring here not to cases of natural smallpox, but to children inoculated against the disease.

Similar misrepresentations in the media occurred following the first anniversary meeting of the Dispensary in June 1784, the year Whitehaven had endured a disastrous smallpox epidemic; 320 cases of smallpox were admitted to the Dispensary, 73 of which resulted in fatality. The actual number of cases and deaths in the town would have been much higher than this. The affluent classes were not included in Dispensary cases and many of the poor people, unable to access the Dispensary by the required letter of recommendation from a Subscriber, would have died without any medical support. 157 children had been 'prepared for the smallpox,' but, 'so strong are the prejudices of many parents', only thirty were eventually inoculated. Rumours again abounded that preparation for smallpox inoculation caused the natural infection with fatal results. Joshua Dixon had to defend his position.

> Several of the newspapers have got egregiously wrong in their accounts of the smallpox patients of the Whitehaven Dispensary. They say 157 children were prepared, of these 30 were inoculated and recovered, and of the remaining 127, no less than 73 took the disorder in a natural way and died. This is very far from the true state published in this paper the 22nd June. (*The Cumberland Pacquet.*) The following is the true state of the Register. 30 children were inoculated and all recovered; 157 were prepared; 320 suffered the natural infection; of these 69 had been prepared; 15 of them died, and 16 of them with difficulty recovered. The whole number of smallpox patients in the natural way were 320,

and the whole number that died was 73, amongst whom were 15 who had been *prepared*, not inoculated.

It is easy to understand how this confusion occurred. A further disquieting fact was that in Whitehaven, inoculation could be offered only during an epidemic of smallpox. In larger cities, where smallpox was endemic, there was a ready supply of material for inoculation. Dixon had to wait for smallpox to be brought into the town by a traveller, before he could obtain material to begin inoculation.

By 1789, Joshua Dixon appeared to be winning the propaganda war in favour of inoculation. In that year, smallpox was introduced into Whitehaven from Liverpool, infecting four children in the same neighbourhood. The practice of quarantine was an important part of the management of smallpox epidemics and sufferers were strictly confined to their houses. The police and magistrates had powers to fine or imprison parents who allowed their infected children to roam the streets. In this instance, 1,131 children in the town were inoculated, 535 in the Dispensary. 771 children had been inoculated in the Dispensary since 1783, with only one death, which Dixon blames neatly on 'improper treatment by its mother'. This compares with forty-six deaths in the 245 children who acquired the natural smallpox.

> Much does it resound to the credit and advantage of this age and kingdom, that a disease which was, for the most part, fatal to one in six persons, and conveyed Deformity or Infirmity to numbers, has become, at this enlightened and benevolent period, in its present or future influence, of very trivial moment.

D R U G G I S T

MARK WYLIE wifhes to inform the Public, that he has just now received a frefh SUPPLY of the very beft MEDICINES and DRUGS from London; — alfo a Quantity of Sweet, Green, Salad, or Common Olive, Whale, Lamp or Train Oils.

The Continuance of Favour from a difcerning Public merits his warmeft Acknowledgements, and an Afsurance that the ftricteft Fidelity and Attention are paid to the Preparation of every Article; and as he has Connections with fome of the firft Houfes in the Drug Line in London, he flatters himfelf that the Quality of his Medicines will be found fuch as will give general Satisfaction.

Phyfician's Prefcriptions faithfully prepared. Ship's Medicine Chefts fitted up, on the fhorteft notice, and moft reafonable terms.

Sold likewife at his Shop, corner of Lowther and King Street, a Variety of Advertifed Medicines, fuch as Anderfon's and Hooper's Pills, Jefuit's Drops, Daffey's and Radcliffe's Elixirs, Godfrey's Cordial, Turlington's Balfam of Life, Stoughton's Drops, and Greenhough's Tincture for Teeth and Gums, Salt of Lemons, &c. &c. &c.

BENEFACTORS
AND SUBSCRIBERS
TO THE
DISPENSARY

WHITEHAVEN Dispensary was a charity, which relied on voluntary subscriptions to finance its affairs. The Dispensary had a robust management structure, with Vice Presidents, Treasurer, Secretary and Auditors, and a monthly management committee. Medical affairs were managed by the Medical Committee, consisting of the Physicians and Surgeons, who gave their time to the Dispensary free of charge. Although a Dispensary had been suggested as early as 1776, it was not until 1783 that sufficient impetus existed in the town for the idea to become reality. William Brownrigg, who had retired from medical practice in Whitehaven in 1770, was an important supporter of the foundation of a Dispensary, and he encouraged his protégée, Joshua Dixon, to become its Physician. The first benefactor of the Dispensary was James Earl of Lonsdale, who donated £100 to the project in 1783. He had inherited the Whitehaven estates in 1755. James was known as 'the bad Earl' due to his manipulative political ways, and was largely an absentee landlord. His benefaction was crucial to the establishment of the Dispensary and although he was annually re-elected as President, there is no record of him ever attending a Dispensary meeting, and he made no further donation to the Charity.

Subscriptions for the Dispensary were solicited in coffee shops and public houses where the regulations of the Dispensary could be perused and discussed. Joshua Dixon, as its chief proponent, worked hard to dispel prejudices and objections, with the result that subscriptions in the first year of the Dispensary totalled £95 15s. The subscribers offer a snapshot of the hierarchy of the town.

Subscribers were listed annually alphabetically, and, within each letter, in descending value of subscription. In 1783, subscriptions ranged from two and sixpence to five guineas. The largest subscription of five guineas was from John Christian Esq. of Curwen Hall, Workington. John Christian (later John Curwen), was born in 1756, the son of Jane Curwen and John Christian. He became High Sheriff of Cumberland in 1784 and was M.P. for Carlisle between 1786 and 1812 before becoming M.P. for Cumberland until his death in 1828. After 1812, he retired from active politics to concentrate on his agricultural interests in and around Workington. He established Friendly or Benefit Societies for his workers by deducting a small levy from their work packets which was paid into a fund to help 'the recovery of the sick, the support of the declining and the education of the young'. To every ten pounds raised in this way, he added three pounds himself. Any member of these societies unable to work because of sickness received five shillings weekly from the fund, until they became fit enough to work again. Doctors' fees were paid from the funds. John Christian Curwen has a well-deserved reputation as a champion of the poor. Although a Dispensary had been established in

Workington around this time, few details remain of its history. As well as giving important financial support to the Whitehaven Dispensary, John Christian served as a Vice President on the Dispensary committee. This support from the major landowner in neighbouring Workington must reflect the good reputation of the Dispensary in Whitehaven.

William Brownrigg M.D., F.R.S. made an annual subscription of two guineas to the Dispensary. Brownrigg was the doyen of Whitehaven practitioners in the eighteenth century and Joshua Dixon's mentor. He studied Medicine at Leiden under Herman Boerhave, graduating in 1736, with a thesis 'De praxi medici ineunda'. He practised as a Physician in Whitehaven from 1737 until the late 1760s, acquiring a national reputation. His marriage in 1741 to Mary, the daughter of Sir James Lowther's agent John Spedding, gave him access to the collieries to conduct scientific experiments on fire and choke damp. He was elected Fellow of the Royal Society in 1742. He published papers on common salt and platinum, as well as on ways of preventing the spread of 'gaol fever'. He retired from medical practice in 1770 to live at his estate at Ormathwaite near Keswick. Brownrigg died in 1800. Joshua Dixon recorded a tribute in his article 'The Literary Life of William Brownrigg', and wrote an obituary for the *Gentleman's Magazine*. Brownrigg's nephew, Anthony Benn, was a local businessman and magistrate, who bailed Brownrigg out of debt in 1787. Benn was an important supporter of the Dispensary and was instrumental in providing funds for the new church in Hensingham in 1791. Benn's death, in 1798, evoked a fulsome tribute from Joshua Dixon in his Annual Report of that year.

Local clergy of all denominations were amongst the first subscribers to the Dispensary. Chief amongst these was the Revd. Wilfrid Huddleston, the Vicar of St. Nicholas, who made an annual subscription of two guineas to the Dispensary and served as Vice-President for over forty years.

Charles Cobb Church, Minister at Holy Trinity subscribed one guinea, as did Revd James Kirkpatrick from the United Reformed Church. Curiously, the Rector of St. James at that time, John Waite, made no subscription to the Dispensary, a situation remedied by his successor, Richard Armistead. On special occasions, collections were made at local churches for the benefit of the Dispensary. One such occasion was New Year, 1785, as noted by the *Cumberland Pacquet*:

> Sunday morning laſt, sermons were preached at the different places of public Worship for the benefit of the Whitehaven Dispensary. It has been thought proper at the commencement of the year, to notice from the pulpit, an Inſtitution which diffuses so much comfort and relief to the unfortunate and indigent.

At the Old Church by Rev. Mr. Huddleſton
From St. Matthew Chap xxv v.40   Collection £8 5s 9d.

At Trinity Church by the Rev. Mr. Church
From 1. Timothy Chap 2 v.15   Collection £7 16s 4d.

At St. James Church by the Rev. Mr. Stephenson
From St. Matthew Chap xxv v.45   Collection £3 0s 3d.

At the Meeting House in High Street by the Rev. Mr. Colquhoun
From St. Matthew Chap xxv v.36-40   Collection £1 3s 10d.

At the Dissenting Chapel in James Street by the Rev. Mr. Kirkpatrick From Colossians Chap 2 Collection £0 17s 11 1/2d

Collected at the Romish Chapel by the Rev. Mr. Johnson
£0 15s 5 ½.

At Lady Huntingdon's Chapel after a sermon by Mr. Jones.
Collection 12s. 10 ½

> It is intended to apply the above to the purpose of adminiſtering relief to poor *Lying-in Women* at their own houses.

> Wednesday laſt, at a meeting held at the Dispensary in Scotch Street, it was resolved to return the Thanks of the Charity to the Eſtablished and Dissenting Clergy in this town for the Sermons preached by them the preceding Sunday in behalf of the said Charity.
>
> It was then also resolved that the Proper Objeḉs of Midwifery Praḉice (viz. the Wives of the moſt indigenous seamen, mechanics and labourers,) be admitted to the Benefits of this Charity by the usual Modes of Recommendation.

The modern custom of Charity performances in the theatre had its equivalent in eighteenth century Whitehaven. A theatre, modelled on the theatre in Bath opened in Roper Street in 1769, and provided a winter season of plays and entertainments by visiting theatre companies. One such company was run by Messrs. Austin and Whitlock, who arranged a charity play for the benefit of the Dispensary on November 30, 1785. Dixon reports that, 'Mr. Howgill Jun. and the Other Musicians very generously relinquished their usual salaries'. £16 12s was Paid to the Dispensary Treasurer following the performance, which ended with a valedictory

JAMES HOGARTH 1726 – 1796.
Benefactor to the Dispensary. Artist unknown
Courtesy of the Beacon, Whitehaven.

address by Mrs. Whitlock in fulsome praise of the Royal Humane Society, and the Whitehaven Dispensary.

A more enigmatic figure in the history of the Dispensary was the linen manufacturer, James Hogarth. In 1788, Hogarth had built 117 cottages for his workers on a site named Mount Pleasant, overlooking the harbour. He also constructed a school, and a church. The church was built with a square tower containing a bell. It contained 133 pews and could hold 1,000 people, making it one of the largest churches in the North of England. Hogarth gave public notice to his tenants in an advert in the *Cumberland Pacquet* of March 20th,1788. The article commented:

> Last week James Hogarth Esq. caused public notice to be given to his tenants,(120 in number) that he will suffer none to remain on his premises, who do not bring their children up in habits of industry and virtue; but that for those who are properly inclined, he proposes erecting a charity school, and furnishing their children with means of suitable instruction, and that the church (which is almost completed) will be opened for the accommodation of both the parents and the children. Employment will also be provided for them in his manufactory.

The Chapel on Mount Pleasant was to have been consecrated by the Bishop of Chester on August 14, 1789. The Bishop arrived in town, but was persuaded not to consecrate the building by the Earl of Lonsdale, who had grown to resent Hogarth's business success. Subsequently the chapel became known only as 'Hogarth's Church', an eponym seized upon gleefully by the *Cumberland Pacquet*:

> We have authority to say that the new Church on Mount Pleasant will not be indebted to the calendar for any name whatsoever. It is to be called "Hogarth's Church." If the idolatry of future times should prefix Saint to the denomination, It will not be the first corruption that has made its way into TITLES.

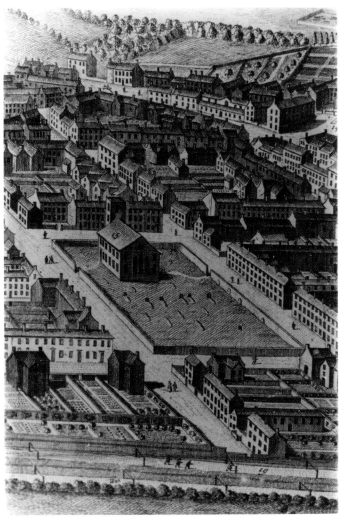

DETAIL FROM A BIRD'S EYE VIEW OF WHITEHAVEN 1738. *Matthias Read.*
The site of the dispensary is the garden in the central foreground. Courtesy of the Beacon, Whitehaven.

In May 1788, Hogarth donated one of his houses, 107 Queen Street, for use as the Dispensary. This donation attracted only a cursory notice in the *Cumberland Pacquet:* 'The Dispensary will shortly be removed from Scotch-Street to the house in Queen-Street with which the Charity has been presented by James Hogarth Esq.' A notice of acknowledgement taken out by the Dispensary Committee was scarcely any more enthusiastic:

> At a general Meeting of the Presidents and Governors holden at the Dispensary in Queen Street on Monday laſt, RESOLVED unanimously. That the thanks of the Presidents, Governors and Subscribers be particularly given to James Hogarth Esq. for his very liberal and unsolicited DONATION of a House, for the use of the said Charity.

> **Peter How Younger,** Secretary

The Dispensary existed in Queen Street rent-free until Hogarth's death in 1796. His executors proved less charitable, and House Rent of five guineas reappears in the Dispensary disbursements for 1797. Although James Hogarth's reputation is based on the donation of 107 Queen Street for use as the Dispensary, in fact, the benefit to the Charity lasted for only eight years. Joshua Dixon reports in 1796 that the Dispensary disbursements exceed the annual subscriptions, which have been diminished by the deaths of major subscribers:

> It muſt, however be acknowledged, that the Disbursements exceed the Annual Receipts; the Price of Medicines being very much enhanced, and the number of Subscribers and Benefactors being diminished: Of the latter, the liberal Donor of the DISPENSARY, for nine years paſt, juſtly claims the affectionate Tribute of our grateful Remembrance. We cannot but deplore that loss which this CHARITY has suſtained in the Death of One who, from its original Eſtablishment, exclusive of a moſt

generous Contribution, has always ſtrenuously endeavoured to promote its Intereſt and recommend it to public Approbation.

James Hogarth, died on March 13, 1796, as reported in the *Pacquet*:

> Sunday laſt in the 71st year of his age, James Hogarth Esq. of Mount Pleasant near this town. He bore his sufferings, which were painful in the extreme, (especially for the laſt seven weeks) with Chriſtian fortitude, and an humble resignation. The moſt remarkable trait in his charaċter (amongſt many other amiable qualities which he possessed) was his boundless and extensive CHARITY to the POOR, who always found in him a FATHER and a FRIEND, and to whom his memory will be ever dear.

Hogarth was buried in a vault under his Chapel tower. The Chapel itself remained unconsecrated as an Anglican church and was used successively by the Methodists, the Primitive Methodists, and finally, in 1899, by the Wesleyan Methodists. It was demolished in 1954.

The death of the Earl of Lonsdale in 1802, gave fresh financial impetus to the Dispensary. The Earl died without an heir, and the Viscounty passed to Sir William Lowther of Swillington, who was entitled the Earl of Lonsdale in 1807. In 1803, Sir William signalled his good intent with a generous benefaċtion of £50 to the Dispensary, and an annual donation of ten guineas thereafter. This placed the Dispensary in a solvent financial position for the next twenty years.

EIGHTEENTH-CENTURY
FEVERS
IN
WHITEHAVEN

THE management of the various types of fever, or 'contagious fever', which regularly plagued the town of Whitehaven, occupied much of Joshua Dixon's work in the Dispensary. The different varieties of fever posed a serious threat to the life and health of the townsfolk. Fevers were classified according to their clinical course. It is likely that different specific infections would be included in the same type of fever. Fevers were known to be contagious as it was common experience, that many fevers spread from person to person, especially in confined and overcrowded situations. Some fevers were part of a recognised clinical syndrome such as measles, smallpox or whooping cough, and here, the relevant clinical term was used to describe the illness. Most fevers, however, did not have the sort of clinical diagnosis we would recognise today, and, instead, are classified in descriptive terms. There are several reasons for this.

A SURGEON BLEEDING THE ARM OF A YOUNG WOMAN WITH A FEVER.

There was controversy over what actually caused disease. Some Physicians subscribed to 'contagionism', the idea that diseases were somehow passed from person to person. Others embraced 'miasmatic theory', which suggested that effluvia from the soil, atmosphere, or patient was the causal factor in disease. Joshua Dixon embraces both philosophies. Pasteur's work, proving that specific microorganisms caused individual diseases, did not occur until the late nineteenth century. Koch's Postulates, the criteria to prove a particular microorganism caused a particular disease, were not published until 1879. Lister's work on antiseptic practice developed around 1865. Joshua Dixon and his contempories, therefore, had little scientific evidence to support their work. Instead, they relied on a ritual of taking the history of the illness, usually from relatives or attendants, followed by a physical examination. In this, the course of the fever was observed, the state of the skin, tongue and urine was assessed and the pulse taken and described. An estimate of the vitality, or otherwise, of the system was made and this determined the type of treatment offered. Despite the dramatic effects of bloodletting, purging and the other remedies offered, there were no drugs, other than 'extracts of the bark' to modify the fever, or treat its underlying cause. The eighteenth-century fever simply ran its course.

Joshua Dixon divided fevers into 'continual', 'remitting' and 'intermittent' types. A continual fever never left the patient throughout the whole course of the disease. If the symptoms were sudden and violent, he labeled it an 'acute' or 'hectic' fever. 'Slow fever' described a prolonged more gentle clinical course with a benign resolution. 'Malignant', 'putrid' or 'petechial' fevers were life threatening illnesses in which the skin became putrid or a petechial rash developed, suggesting a septicaemia in modern terms. A remitting fever waxed and waned throughout the illness without ever leaving the patient. An ague, or intermittent fever, was a prolonged illness with periods of remission lasting one to four days, often associated with exposure to a marshy environment. Malaria would be a possible cause.

'Nervous fever' was a broad term, which Dixon applied to any fever accompanied by symptoms of the central nervous system. These might have included headaches, convulsions or delirium. In later years, he uses the term 'continued fever' to describe the same group of illnesses. Other Dispensaries prefer 'putrid fever'. It now seems clear that the terms nervous, continued and putrid fevers were interchangeable and included a variety of different diseases, not all of them infectious. Enteric fevers, such as typhoid, febrile illnesses of childhood with convulsions, and typhus fever were part of this complex. Typhus, or gaol fever, was common where conditions were overcrowded with poor hygiene. Typhus is caused by a rickettsial organism transmitted by insects, chiefly body lice. After an incubation period of five days, there is an abrupt onset with high fever, headache and prostration. A rash appears after five days. Peripheral gangrene may occur. The illness lasts about three weeks and, if left untreated has a sixty per cent mortality rate. Typhoid fever is caused by the Salmonella group of organisms and is transmitted by the faecal contamination of food and water. Overcrowding and poor sanitation would encourage the spread of typhoid. The illness progresses through fever, myalgia, headache, profuse diarrhoea and a characteristic rash. Mortality would be of the order of twenty per cent.

Joshua Dixon has recorded every case of nervous fever he encountered during his forty-year tenure of the office of Physician to the Dispensary. He describes the epidemiology of the illness, showing that it is very infectious, and often recurs. In 1783, 371 cases of nervous fever occurred, of which ten ended in death. Favourable cases ran a prolonged course with a series of remissions beginning on the eleventh day, and recovery on about day seventeen. Fatal cases were more acute and generally terminated between the ninth and eleventh day without any remission. According to Dixon, 'fatal terminations of this fever chiefly occurred to those, who, having previously indulged in an intemperate mode of conduct, were rather advanced in life, and the first victims of its virulency.' His management was uncompromising:

> The methods and precautions generally recommended, and found by experience highly qualified to eradicate this infectious disease or totally interrupt its further baneful communication have been everywhere strenuously inculcated; and so far as the circumstances of the sick would permit, diligently executed. Fumigations with camphire, myrrh, sulphur, tobacco or juniper berries and the explosion of gunpowder were deemed the most efficacious antidotes to this contagion. The strictest observance of cleanliness, with regard to the patients, their families and habitations, was also required; and a free circulation of air, from various apertures in the windows and doors, always admitted. To these salutary expedients, were frequently added the liberal application of vinegar to the floors, bedsteads etc., and fresh prepared whitewash to the floors and ceilings of infected places. The bedcloaths and linen of the sick were directed to be steeped several hours in cold water, then washed and dried in the open air, with a view to prevent the pernicious effects of contaminated effluvia.

The tabular arrangement of the cases of Nervous fever, presented by Joshua Dixon in1785, allows speculation as to the nature of the illness. The fever affects all ages from the very young to the elderly, and is unlikely therefore to be a single entity. Although Dixon declares the town free of Nervous Fever in June 1786, it is only a couple of months before it makes its reappearance, this time courtesy of a boy from Ireland. It seems an endemic problem rather than an occasional epidemic. Fatal cases are mainly in older adults. The Dispensary, under Joshua Dixon's direction, has a clear public health role and takes responsibility for recording and preventing epidemics of 'Contagious Fever.' Dixon was a true medical pioneer and anticipates the role of Medical Officer of Health by one hundred years.

Later in 1786, Dixon reports:

> The only remaining contagion of any consequence was Nervous Fever. In the month of June laſt, the town was perfectly free of its influence, and remained so till the latter end of Auguſt when a Boy (who took the disease in Dublin) unhappily conveyed it into a very confined yet well inhabited situation. Several persons in the neighbourhood were soon after seized with its urgent symptoms, suffering a tedious and dangerous malady.
>
> This FEVER has since been communicated, and notwithſtanding every exertion, to prevent or mitigate its malignancy, became, in many inſtances, a not less painful than deſtructive diſtemper. The diet of the poor, with the want of cleanliness and free ventilation, inevitably exposes them to an active and powerful infection.
>
> With a view to anticipate or remove these disadvantages, every requisite attention and admonition have been assiduously recommended and in moſt cases exactly fulfilled. The impropriety and hazard of visiting the sick were ſtrenuously insiſted on; since perhaps no circumſtance has more certainly contributed to diffuse the contagion than this incautious and unnecessary connection with infected persons and places. To dissipate and correct its virulency, the frequent admission of a full ſtream of air, and the application of the usual antidotes, especially the various fumigating articles, were always particularly enjoined. In order, also, to enable the attendants upon the sick, and their families, to resiſt the power of that contagion they are unavoidably and conſtantly exposed to, the inſtant removal of linen etc., replete with the noxious effluvia, and where possibly admissible, the use of a more generous diet, with the liberal employment of Cordials, and the Bark, would be eligible. This laſt as the beſt means of reſtoring the energy of the syſtem, may certainly be deemed equally efficacious in supporting it.

Dixon made a clear distinction between Nervous Fever, and epidemic influenza, which would also affect all age groups and be more fatal in the elderly. He recognises and describes epidemics of Influenza, recording, for example in 1788.

From the above period till the beginning of August, the lower class of people were remarkably healthy. During this month, and the two following, an Influenza, chiefly characterised by the symptoms of inflammatory catarrh, almost universally prevailed. This disease had already diffused its contagious influence over the whole of the Kingdom, and that of Ireland. A febrile tendency, preceded by considerable lassitude and weakness, accompanied those affections of the head, throat and chest by which it was peculiarly distinguished. Though sometimes virulent and dangerous, when attacking relaxed and languid constitutions, or where there was a manifest disposition to consumptive disorder, it appeared for the most part very mild, and rarely of more than three days continuance. THIRTEEN of the Epidemics have raged very generally in Europe, since the beginning of this century. We can also, tho with less accuracy, trace in past ages, the previous recurrence of ELEVEN similar contagions.

Other Dispensaries classified fevers in a different way. The Newcastle Dispensary did not use the term nervous fever, preferring putrid fever. Joshua Dixon's counterpart in Carlisle, John Heysham clearly had a facility to recognise Typhus Fever as a distinct entity. As early as 1782, he published an account of 'Jail Fever', or Typhus, as it appeared in Carlisle in 1781.

The danger of exposure to Contagious Fevers was not confined to the relatives of the patient. Following the death of William Robinson, the position of Apothecary to the Dispensary had become vacant in September 1789. An election for the vacancy was held at a General Meeting on October 9. Candidates were advised to 'signify their intentions at least fourteen days before the day of election'. Each subscriber could vote in proportion to the value of his subscription. 'A subscriber of one guinea has one vote, a benefactor of ten guineas two votes, and so on, in proportion, not exceeding ten votes.' The successful applicant was Mr. William Christian Little. His tenure as Apothecary was brief. The use of the word 'malignant' in this extract from 1789, refers not to its current usage as a synonym for cancers, but to its original meaning of a bad or malevolent nature.

The Friends of this Institution will affectionately deplore the Death of Mr. William Christian Little, who from the impulse of Inclination, rather than Duty, assiduously and faithfully fulfilled the various obligations of apothecary to the Charity. Whilst sedulously attentive to a family of four persons confined in one bed in a noxious apartment, where malignant disease had long and virulently prevailed, he received that Contagion, which, in the space of eleven days, terminated a most useful existence.

Mr. William Christian Little was elected Apothecary to the Dispensary on the 9th of October last, and died on the 12th of May, sincerely regretted by all concerned in the management of this Charity.

TALES

OF

SUSPENDED ANIMATION

O<small>NCE</small> the Dispensary was established, one of Joshua Dixon's priorities, was to annexe the Charity to the London Humane Society. In the report for 1783, he writes:

> Regardful of our maritime situation, and the dangers to which we are inevitably exposed, it was deemed eligible to form a connection with the L<small>ONDON</small> H<small>UMANE</small> S<small>OCIETY</small>, and very generally, to distribute its judicious instructions, procuring at the same time a complete apparatus for the recovery of persons apparently drowned. The modes of treatment best adapted to restore such deplorable objects will now be universally known, and the intelligent of every profession are earnestly requested occasionally to put them in immediate and vigorous execution.

Two London Physicians, William Hawes and Thomas Cogan, had founded the London Humane Society, later the Royal Humane Society, in 1774. Both men were pioneers of the new medical technique of resuscitation, and were concerned at the frequency with which death was misdiagnosed, leading in some cases to burial alive.

This was particularly likely to occur as a result of prolonged immersion in water. In the late eighteenth century, children were not taught to swim and in 1773, the year before the society was founded, 123 people had drowned in London. The society was initially called 'The Society for the Recovery of Persons Apparently Drowned'. It published information on techniques of saving drowning people and instituted a system of rewards for rescuers. Thus, four guineas were paid to anyone bringing a person back to life, and one guinea to anyone allowing their house to be used for the reception of a drowned person. Branches of the Society were established in ports and coastal towns where the risk of drowning was high. The technique was also used for victims of gas poisoning or accidents in the coal mines.

In August 1783, the local newspaper reported:

> At a meeting of the Committee of Whitehaven Dispensary held on Wednesday last at the Dispensary in Scotch Street, it was resolved 'That a complete Apparatus for the purpose of recovering persons apparently drowned, or suffering from suffocation or suspension, be immediately procured from the Humane Society in London, for the use of this Charity.' Dr. Hawes and Mr. Sherwen of Enfield, (who is a Medical Assistant to the Humane Society), have been consulted on the business and have forwarded printed directions of the mode of treatment etc. with their future wishes for the success of this undertaking. They have also recommended to the committee the use of an instrument, which has lately been presented to the Society by Dr. Coggin of Amsterdam. This instrument is not unlike the grapple of a long boat, and is found very useful in most expeditiously catching the bodies of drowning people.
>
> We are since informed that the apparatus is now on the road, and that Dr. Hawes is so highly pleased with the exertions of the committee in instituting so laudable an undertaking, that he has made them a compliment of the instrument above mentioned, and by way of exciting in others that spirit of humanity for which he is not less eminent than for his great abilities in his profession, he intends meeting the next General Court day, that one of the

Society's gold medals, (with the inscription, on the one side *Hor pretium Cive servato, tulit, and on the other Fortifan Scintillula lateat*[1].) be given to the gentleman who shall attend the first successful case of re-animation at Whitehaven. A general letter addressed to Dr. Joshua Dixon accompanies the apparatus.

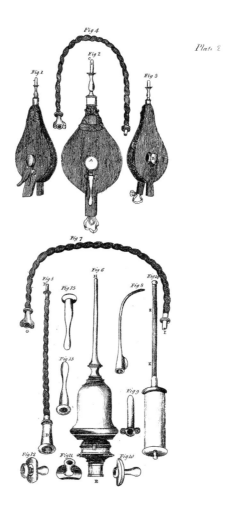

BELLOWS AND PIPES FOR ARTIFICIAL RESPIRATION 1771. Wellcome Library London.

1. Translated from the Latin this means, *'He earned this reward by saving a citizen'*, and, *'The spark of life may lay hidden.'*

Whitehaven Dispensary was the first in the country to include resuscitation from drowning in its services. Newcastle Dispensary, for example, although founded in 1777, did not include 'a department for preserving the lives of those apparently dead' until 1789. Writing in the *Cumberland Pacquet* in October 1783, Peter How Younger, the Dispensary Secretary, published a letter from 'so very eminent a character as Dr. Hawes' congratulating the Dispensary on its innovative thinking.

The recommendations of the Humane Society for the 'Recovery of Persons Apparently Drowned' were first made in 1774, and consisted of four main directives.

It was suggested that the body should be laid down with the head a little raised, and then dried, warmed and rubbed. Common practices of the time, such as suspending the body by the ankles to encourage the water to run out, or rolling the body in a barrel, were not recommended.

In order to restore respiration, one nostril should be occluded by an assistant, and air blown into the lungs through the other nostril by means of a wooden pipe or bellows. The lungs were then deflated by gently pushing on the chest with both hands.

Whilst this artificial respiration was taking place, another assistant was encouraged to introduce tobacco smoke into the large bowel by means of a flexible rubber tube passed through the anus, attached to a fumigating apparatus, which burned tobacco. This was based on the observation that, after death, the bowels retained their irritability long after any other organ, and could be stimulated when all else had failed.

Finally, as a last resort, bronchotomy, a surgical opening of the air passages in the chest, or bleeding could be tried. The apparatus for the 'Recovery of Drowned Persons' provided for the Dispensary by the Humane Society consisted of two pairs of bellows and four small pipes for blowing into the nostrils. The fumigator was a brass box with a handle. To encourage the burning tobacco, air was pumped into the box using bellows via an ivory pipe. The ensuing tobacco smoke was introduced into the anus via a flexible tube. The cost of the apparatus was £1 9s 6d.

The *Cumberland Pacquet* reported the first successful rescue from drowning on May 17, 1785:

> Tuesday laſt, as three boys were playing in a boat in Parton Harbour, while the tide was in, the boat overset, and one of them (Robert Steele), a child of five years old, was with difficulty got out of the water and without any sign of life. A messenger was sent to this town and an account of the accident being received at the Dispensary, while the Physician was attending the business of the Charity, he immediately set off with the Apparatus provided by the Society, and, on his arrival, had the happiness to find that the methods recommended by the Society had been begun and apparently with success. After persevering some time, and making the applications prescribed by the Humane Society, the child was happily reſtored to life, and seems now perfeƈtly recovered.
>
> It is owing to those firſt employed on the body that the nobleſt of all human achievements has been made,-the life of a fellow creature has been preserved:- but it will not be deemed a detraƈtion from the applause they are juſtly entitled to, seriously to remonſtrate againſt the praƈtice of rolling the body. The Humane Society in London has declared it a pernicious cuſtom and it had nearly proved fatal in this inſtance. The Whitehaven Dispensary provided a sufficient number of the rules and methods of treatment, furnished by Dr. Hawes. The good intentions of those who may be casually employed in such human exercises will be beſt answered by a ſtriƈt adherence to the rules- they are founded on great judgement and repeated experiment.

ROYAL HUMANE SOCIETY
FUMIGATING APPARATUS 1771.
Wellcome Library London.

This episode is remarkable for several reasons. The distance of Parton Harbour from the Whitehaven Dispensary was two miles with the hill of Bransty intervening. It seems that both the messenger and the Physician travelled on foot, the latter carrying the prescribed apparatus. Contemporary portraits of the Physician do not suggest his progress would be speedy. It seems likely that up to two hours must have elapsed between the incident and the attendance of the Physician, making the recovery of little Robert Steele even more remarkable. This does not deter Joshua Dixon from berating the rescuers for the 'pernicious custom of rolling the body.'

A similar instance of recovery from 'Suspended Animation' was reported in the *Cumberland Pacquet* on August 26, 1789:

> Laſt Sunday morning, James Somerville, a boy about 14 years of age, had gone into the water to bathe, and was swimming near the outer end of the North Wall, when he was seized with the cramp, and sank before any aſsiſtance could be given. After being under water about seven minutes, he was found and taken out by the harbour-boat, apparently dead. The body was conveyed to a convenient place, and, the apparatus being brought from the Dispensary, the means, recommended by the Humane Society, were employed, and in about ten minutes, the symptoms of returning life were discovered, and, in less than an hour, he was perfectly recovered.

Dixon includes the incident in his Annual Report for 1789, paying due regard to the four surgeons who effected the recovery.

> Laſt Sunday with regard to the deplorable subjeƈts of SUSPENDED ANIMATION, by whatever means induced, (another salutary Appendage to this DISPENSARY) as they naturally claim, so they shall always obtain our diligent and affeƈtionate exertions. Impelled by the genuine diƈtates and beſt principles of HUMANITY, a more supreme satisfaƈtion can never be

experienced, than when we are thus administering to the most dreadful temporal contingency. And if such endeavour prove eventually successful (for frequent and generally insuperable are it's obstacles) no source of exquisite felicity can, in these instances, equal that of restoring life to an expiring or apparently expired FELLOW CREATURE; and whose fate must have been otherwise inevitably determined.

This felicity fortunately occurred to the gentlemen (Messrs ISAAC and JOHN WILLIAMSON, EDWARD DAWSON, JOHN GAITSKELL and WILLIAM C. LITTLE, Surgeons) who judiciously and assiduously effected the extraordinary recovery of JAMES SOMERVILLE *. In which case, a strict observance of those instructions so liberally supplied by the ingenious REGISTER of the ROYAL HUMANE SOCIETY (whose beneficent regard to the various Interests of this Charity shall be ever gratefully acknowledged) and especially the employment of the FUMIGATING APPARATUS, gave the first indication of returning LIFE and afterwards, perfectly restored it.

*The particulars of this singular instance of RESUSCITATION after a detention of Seven Minutes beneath the surface of the water, are enumerated in the CASE and REPORT BOOKS of the DISPENSARY."

The *Cumberland Pacquet* reported the incident as:

…the first of restoring suspended animation, that has occurred in this place. The body had lain seven minutes at the bottom of the water; some minutes elapsed in conveying it to a house, and procuring the apparatus from the Dispensary, and the recovery was effected after about an hour's application. But the patient remained insensible for some time, and it was not until about three hours afterwards, that he had any recollection of the incident. The COMMITTEE very cheerfully paid the rewards recommended by the HUMANE SOCIETY (which forms a part of the Public Charity under the name of WHITEHAVEN DISPENSARY) viz. 5 shillings to the boatmen, who took the body out of the water, 5 shillings and ten pence to the person who carried to the house, and ten shillings and sixpence to the house that received it.

By 1790, Dixon had recorded four cases where recovery occurred despite a situation, 'where the vital functions were, seemingly, in great measure, totally suspended'. He advised the employment of all methods of resuscitation, even in 'the most discouraging circumstances, when every appearance of life has been long extinguished.' To this end, 600 sheets and pocket plans of instructions from the Royal Humane Society were distributed in the town and surrounding countryside, 'wherever it was apprehended accidents by water might occur'.

THE ANNIVERSARY MEETING
of the PRESIDENTS AND GOVERNORS
of the WHITEHAVEN DISPENSARY
will be held at the Dispensary in Scotch St.
on Monday *June* 13th, 1785, at 12 o-clock.

The general report will be made and the ſtate of the charity publiſhed ſhortly thereafter, for the ſatisfaction of thoſe who have contributed towards that moſt uſeful inſtitution and for the benefit of others who may be induced to further its laudable and benevolent intentions.

At the GENERAL ANNIVERSARY MEETING of the Preſidents, Governors and Subſcribers of the WHITEHAVEN DISPENSARY, held on *June* 11th, 1787, it was RESOLVED UNANIMOUSLY:

That the THANKS of the ſaid Preſidents, Governors and Subſcribers be given to JOSHUA DIXON M.D., the Phyſician, MR. JOHN HAMILTON, the Surgeon, Mr. Henry Fletcher, the Treaſurer, and Mr. Peter How Younger, the Secretary, for their great and diſintereſted Attention to the Buſineſs of the Charity.

☞ By Order of the Governors,
PETER HOW YOUNGER   Secretary.

OFFICERS for the YEAR 1790.

PRESIDENT

The Right Honourable James Earl of Lonſdale

VICE PRESIDENTS

John Chriſtian Curwen, Eſq. | Anthony Benn, Eſq.

William Brownrigg, M. D. and F.R.S.

Rev. Wilfrid Huddleſton. | Rev. C.C. Church.

TREASURER.   SECRETARY.

Mr. Robert Blakeney.   Mr. Peter How Younger.

AUDITORS.

Robert Fiſher, Eſq. | Rr. John Wilſon.

Mr. Joſeph Bell.

COMMITTEE

John Hartley, Eſq. | Thomas Hartley, Eſq.

Robert Fiſher, Eſq. | James Hogarth, Eſq.

Mr. Benjamin Gilliat. | Mr. Robert Blakeney.

Mr. R. Fletcher, Merchant. | Mr. H. Fletcher.

Mr. R. Fletcher, Mercer | Mr. Thomas Fiſher.

Mr. Joſeph Bell | Mr. John Johnſton.

PHYSICIAN.

Joſhua Dixon, M.D.

SURGEON EXTRAORDINARY.

Mr. John Hamilton

SURGEON.

Mr. Joſeph Harris.

APOTHECARY.

Mr. Joſeph Gunſon.

A DAY IN THE LIFE
OF THE
DISPENSARY, 1790

AT nine o'clock on a grey morning in late November 1790, the Apothecary, Mr. Joseph Gunson, opened the door of the Dispensary at 107 Queen Street. A huddle of people waited outside, sheltering in the lee of the building from the drizzling rain blowing in from the harbour. Most of those waiting were from the poorest parts of the town, cold, bedraggled, hungry and wet. Two men stood out from the rest. Dressed in top hats and coats, they were important subscribers to the Dispensary, and the apothecary admitted them first. Anthony Benn, a distinguished magistrate, had been one of the first subscribers to the Dispensary, and his companion, Thomas Hartley was a prominent merchant in the town. Their purpose was to alert the Physician to several cases of contagious fever in Tangier Street, and to complete letters of recommendation to the Dispensary requesting that the Physician visit these patients at home. Patients wishing to be visited that day were required to send their letters of recommendation to the Dispensary promptly at nine o'clock. The apothecary entered details of these cases into the home visiting ledger, and arranged the visits by degree of urgency and district. The letters of recommendation were presented in an orderly arrangement to the Physician, when he attended at ten o'clock. The regulations stipulated that letters presented later than this would not attract a visit until the next day. Having attended to the business of the Subscribers, the apothecary turned his attention to the waiting patients.

The apothecary's room was small, and cluttered with the tools of his trade. Glass bottles of white, blue, red, in all shapes and sizes, vials, pestles, powders, and mysterious liquids graced his shelves. He conducted his business from a small desk and chair next to the burning coals in the grate. The patients jostled for a place near the fire. Outpatients who presented their letters before ten o'clock were seen that day, initially by the apothecary. The poorest patients, unable to obtain a letter of recommendation, simply turned up at the Dispensary, and were assessed by the apothecary. By ten o'clock, when the Physician arrived, some semblance of order had been brought to the business of the day.

On an average day, about ten patients presented themselves to the Dispensary. Some of these were 'trivial cases', with minor illness or injuries. The apothecary attended to these patients himself. Most were 'dismissed with advice only'.

Patients with serious illness or contagious fever were seen by the Physician. They were examined in one of the two consultation rooms. A prescription was written, in Latin, on their letter of recommendation. The preparation of the medication was delegated to the apothecary's apprentices, and this often took several hours. Finally the medicines were dispensed by the apothecary, 'affixing to each medicine the patient's name and the manner of using it'. The routine outpatient business was completed by noon. Inoculation against smallpox was offered, probably on a weekly basis by one of the surgeons available to the Dispensary. Midwifery was also included in the Dispensary practice. In the first six months of 1786, sixty-five pregnant women had been admitted for delivery, and there were ninety-two 'midwifery patients' admitted in the following year. By 1790, 626 midwifery cases had been admitted to the Dispensary. Injuries, accidents and other emergencies arising during the day were dealt with by one of the surgeons on an on-call basis. These were Mr. John Hamilton, (whose title 'Surgeon Extraordinary' was awarded for heroic management of a ruptured popliteal artery aneurysm) and Mr. Joseph Harris. The apothecary, Joseph Gunson, had been an Army surgeon, and later did practise in the Dispensary as a surgeon.

As noon approached, the Treasurer of the Dispensary, Mr. Robert Blakeney, arrived to conduct the financial business of the Charity. Blakeney was a customs officer in the port of Whitehaven. As the month end approached, he had several accounts to settle. Although a bank had opened in Whitehaven in 1786, all the Dispensary transactions were made in cash. Joseph Gunson's monthly salary as apothecary was three pounds, and wine for the many fever patients that year was costing almost two pounds each month. Four pounds was due to Mark Wylie, the main druggist in town, who supplied drugs and medicines to the Dispensary, and there were smaller bills for printing, coal, candles and whitewash. Later, the Secretary, Mr. Peter How Younger, arrived. Younger was a member of the How family of tobacco merchants, who had become bankrupt when the tobacco trade collapsed. He was a local attorney, a powerful man in the town who held several important secretarial appointments including the magistrates and the Harbour Board. The agenda for the half-yearly general meeting in December had to be agreed with the Physician, including a proposal to award a gold medallion to John Hamilton in recognition of his great service as surgeon to the Dispensary.

With the administrative business of the day over, the Physician set out on foot to visit selected patients 'in their own habitations'. The regulations advised that in the case of acute diseases and fevers the Physician should visit 'frequently', while the apothecary should visit these cases at least once a day. In November 1790, the town was subject to yet another epidemic of a 'malignant nervous fever', and on this day, the Physician had to make visits to infected houses in Tangier Street, in nearby Chapel Street, and in the New Houses. He would treat the early stages of the fever with an emetic, usually ipecacuahna syrup, using decoctions of serpentaria or a preparation of opium for sedation if necessary. In the later stages of the illness, when the system needed stimulation, mosch, camphor, digitalis and extracts of cinchona bark were his favourite remedies. Patients visited at home were advised to keep their letters of recommendation under cover 'to preserve them clean'. This allowed the Physician to write his prescription on the letter, which was then taken to the Dispensary to obtain the medicines. Patients were required to 'behave themselves decently and soberly, and strictly conform to the directions of the Physician or surgeon, other wise they shall be immediately dismissed.' In addition to treating the patients, the Physician was rigorous in his attempts to contain and prevent the spread of infection. This involved the introduction of several of the 'prophylactics', including the washing of contaminated articles of clothing, an attempt to purify the atmosphere by the explosion of gunpowder, fumigations of tobacco or aromatic herbs and camphor, and in the longer term, the application of whitewash to the walls.

In chronic diseases, when the patient was confined to his house and unable to attend the Dispensary, the regulations advised that the Physician should prescribe 'occasionally', and give necessary directions. In such cases, the apothecary was expected to visit twice weekly and report any change to the Physician. The experience of visiting a house and finding the patient out remains a familiar frustration: 'In diseases which do not confine the patients constantly to their houses, a Physician, when visiting, will often find them abroad: it is therefore proper that such patients should attend the Dispensary at the stated hours and days to receive advice.'

Of course, many of the patients visited with chronic illnesses would eventually succumb. The statutes of the Newcastle Dispensary offered guidelines on this:

> As no exception is made to the admission of incurable disease, a very considerable number of patients upon the Doctor's list are confined by consumptions in the last stage, by dropsies, palsies and other diseases proceeding from wore out constitutions, or the decay of old age. Although in such cases, death be inevitable, yet humanity will prompt a Physician to contribute every aid from Medicine in order to alleviate the most painful symptoms: but the frequent attendance of a Physician in such cases would take up time which might be more essentially employed towards the relief of others.

The Physician therefore played an advisory role in home visiting. The apothecary, who would visit critical cases two or three times daily, did most of the home visits. When patients were 'cured or relieved', they were expected to return their letters of recommendation to the Dispensary, and acknowledge their gratitude to their recommenders. This enabled the Physician to maintain an accurate record of outcomes. Cured patients were given a printed ticket from the Dispensary certifying their cure, and asked to present this at their respective parish churches on the following Sunday, 'to give thanks'.

The work of the Dispensary continued well into the evening. The apothecary and his apprentice had to complete the preparation of the day's prescriptions. Powders were ground, solutions mixed and diluted, tinctures were assimilated, tonics and opiates prepared, juniper berries ground, and myrrh and camphor bound with vinegar, all to the candle's flickering flame. For the Physician too, the evening had its regular duties. The day's episodes of disease were carefully recorded and indexed, and the outcome written down. This enabled the Physician to report the annual incidence and outcomes of all illnesses he encountered in the Dispensary in the system of classification devised by 'the ingenious Dr. Cullen'. Joshua Dixon's Annual Reports of the Whitehaven Dispensary from 1783–1823, are unique in the Dispensary movement, and establish Dixon as one of the greatest dispensary Physicians in the country.

Dispensaries have sometimes been compared to present day outpatient clinics. Whitehaven Dispensary bears an uncanny resemblance to my own experience of rural general practice. Nothing typifies this more than the small surgery at Rowrah House in West Cumbria, at the end of the twentieth century. Rowrah House had been the house and surgery of Dr. J. Haythornthwaite, the village doctor in the early twentieth century, and now functioned as a branch surgery of a larger practice. Here was a small waiting room, with school benches for the patients, and an even smaller consulting room, where the lack of basic amenities made examination of the patient hazardous. The Physician attended daily at an appointed hour. The patients meanwhile had been marshalled into order by the resident Apothecary, Mrs. Joyce Elliot, who practised from her kitchen in Rowrah House. Her Dispensary, gloriously free from any qualification or regulation, was her kitchen table, laden with drugs, medicines, linctuses, dressings and suppositories, all in no particular order. The Physician's prescriptions were dispensed here. Like the eighteenth-century apothecary, Joyce Elliot had a small practice of her own, dispensing advice and medicines to this isolated rural community during the hours the Physician was absent elsewhere. In cases where the Physician was needed urgently, the apothecary placed a red Elastoplast tin in the Dispensary window, to alert a passing Physician that his opinion was required.

————

An ACCOUNT of the PATIENTS admitted, from JUNE 14th, 1790, to JUNE 13th, 1791.

Recommended and Regiſtered (of whom 1000 were attended in their reſpective Habitations) • •	2193
Midwifery Objects • • • • • • • •	108
Trivial Caſes • • • • • • • •	1420
	3721
Patients remaining upon the Books June 14, 1790	227
Total	3948

————

The STATE of the REGISTERS.

Cured • • • • • • • • •	2108
Relieved • • • • • • • • •	55
Incurable • • • • • • • • •	30
Irregular • • • • • • • • •	3
Dead • • • • • • • • • •	52
Remain upon the Books • • • • • •	172
	2420

Total Number of PATIENTS admited fince the Inftitution of this CHARITY, *June* 30, 1783.

In 1783	•	•	•	2057
In 1784	•	•	•	2644
In 1785	•	•	•	3034
In 1786	•	•	•	2708
In 1787	•	•	•	2521
In 1788	•	•	•	2129
In 1789	•	•	•	5996
In 1790	•	•	•	3721

24810

Cured	•	•	•	13340
Relieved	•	•	•	497
Incurable	•	•	•	169
Irregular	•	•	•	26
Dead	•	•	•	466
Remain upon the Books				172

14670

The Number of Patients admitted
(as by the foregoing Lift) • • • • • • 24810

Regiftered Patients	•	•	•	•	•	•	14 670
Midwifery Cafes	•	•	•	•	•	•	626
Trivial Cafes	•	•	•	•	•	•	9514

Total 24,810

Total Subfcriptions
and Benefactions £.123 7 6
In the Charity Box 1 17 7½

COLLECTIONS.

Old Chapel 9 12 7½

Trinity { Generally col-
lected 7l.16s.
6½d.
From theHens-
ingham Friendly
Society 2l. 2s.o. } 9 18 6½

St. James's 5 00 0½
Meeting houfe in James's
  Street 1 17 4½
Meeting Houfe in High
  Street 1 13 5½
Romifh Chapel 0 14 0
Lady Huntingdon's
  Chapel 0 11 3
Cafh Lent 100 0 0
Intereft of Do. 5 0 0
Do. Of furplus cafh
£2 3s 8d
Lofs by bad filver } 1 19 1¾
4s 6 1/4d
Balance with the
  Treafurer laft year 33 12 10½

Total £.295 4 5¼
Difburfements 134 9 1

Balance £.160 15 4¼

DISBURSEMENTS.

Drugs and Medicines 43 10 4
Wine 21 7 8½
Midwifery Expences 12 7 6
Printing and Stationary 7 2 4½
Coals, Candles, Boy's
Attendance,
Carriage of
Drugs, Phials,
Leather,
And fundry
fmall Articles 11 13 2
Apothecary's Salary
and Gratuity 38 08 0

£.134 09 1

SUBSCRIPTIONS are taken in at the TREASURER's; at WARE's
PRINTING-OFFICE; and at the DISPENSARY.

Blank letters of Recommendation *may be had at the* Difpenfary.

A TRIBUTE

ON THE DEATH OF

WILLIAM BROWNRIGG

Wiliam Brownrigg, M.D. F.R.S.
1712–1800

THE immediate CONDUCTORS of this CHARITY are
earneſtly disposed to express with Gratitude and
Eſteem, their beſt Acknowledgments of that Obligation
which the Liberality of the Wealthy and Affectionate has
conferred on it. Especially do they wish to thankfully atteſt
the Beneficence of those, who influenced by Motives of
disinterested Philanthropy, have long promoted its Views;
and now, distantly situated, can no longer experience
its salutary Influence. The very numerous Additions of
respeƈtable Names to the Liſt of *Annual Subscribers* obtained
this Year, and the voluntary Aids of *Private Benefaƈtors* are
also moſt gratefully announced. Their Generosity enables
this humane Endowment to perfeƈtly fulfil its original
Designations: and amply supplies that Deficiency in its
Funds which the Death and Removal of several worthy

N.B. This chapter is an extract from Joshua Dixon's Annual Report for 1799.

PORTRAIT BY JOSHUA DIXON, THOUGHT TO BE OF WILLIAM BROWNRIGG.
Wellcome Library, London.

Contributors had occasioned. Of these it may be juſtly expected that we should moſt regardfully notice the late ingenious Doctor BROWNRIGG, who, prior to the Eſtablishment of MEDICAL CHARITIES in this County, declared his Sentiments in Favour of such INSTITUTIONS, fully assured that they were not only qualified to relieve suffering Indigency, but also to accomplish the salutary Design he had oft zealously agitated; that of suppressing the Power, and interrupting the Progress of Contagious Disease. Actuated by these Inducements, the DOCTOR became an early very liberal Subscriber; and as he was then an acting Magiſtrate, a Vice President to this DISPENSARY. From these Considerations it will appear eligible to close this INTRODUCTION to our present REPORT, with the following *General Observations* relative to the laudable and useful Pursuits of this eminent Practitioner.

The Celebrity which Doctor BROWNRIGG deservedly obtained in the Exercise of his Profession, during a Period of Thirty Years, might have been predicted by the favourable Circumſtances attending his primary Attachment to it. Intimately acquainted with the Classics, and an excellent Mathematician, he was perfectly enabled to prosecute the general literary and philosophical Studies, which are requisite Preliminaries to that of the SCIENCE of MEDICINE. His Proficiency in those Studies, and Attainments in that Science, were readily acknowledged, not only by the *Literati* of this Kingdom, but by the moſt illuſtrious *Professors* of the Continent; with whom he was either personally intimate, or supported a regular Correspondence. They were indeed, certainly proved by his numerous, elaborate and beneficial Writings* He endeavoured by accurate and repeated Experiments, to disclose the latent Operations of Nature; and the present well eſtablished Doctrines, relative to the Properties of the various Gasses, may certainly be imputed to his Discoveries respecting them: as he was unqueſtionably the Inventor of those Principles which formed the Basis whereon the permanent Syſtem of *Chemical Philosophy* is now erected.

As the experienced PHYSICIAN, the professional Judgement of Doctor BROWNRIGG, in his native County, attained the higheſt Eſtimation; unremitting and moſt judicious were his Endeavours to eradicate, relieve, or prevent the Communication of peſtilent Contagions: whilſt an equal Degree of Discernment and Assiduity was exerted to alleviate the Urgency of chronic Infirmities and Diſtempers. But the sureſt Proof of his medical Consequence may be adduced from that frequent Application which was made to him, by his opulent Friends, in all Cases of Difficulty and Danger; long after, with a View to possess the *Otium cum Dignitate*[2], he had relinquished actual Practice.

From this general Statement it may be properly inferred, that to the Abilities of Doctor BROWNRIGG, as a chemical Philosopher, or dogmatic Physician, the higheſt Degree of Respectability will ever attach itself.

To this, the public, might be briefly annexed the private Character of the MAN, juſtly eſtimated not less *good* than *great.* Amiable and polite in his Behaviour, with a peculiar attention to oblige, his Society was always earneſtly solicited. A humane Disposition, an unprejudiced Judgement, benevolent Affections, and an accurate taſte for polite Literature, were in him happily united: and his Life, extended to a long Period, was diſtinguished by the Purity and Integrity of his Morals, the Elegance of his Manners, the Mildness of his Temper, and the undeviating Regard which he paid to religious Obligations.

Of the merits of this excellent Man, thus imperfectly delineated, his intimate Friends and the Society which he adorned, will ever retain an affectionate Remembrance: whilſt this Country muſt long venerate and eſteem his MEMORY; to which it will assuredly pay the *juſt Tribute* of

2. Translated from the Latin this means, *'Peace with dignity.'*

Gratitude and Respect: –

> Vivit *adhuc inter Bonos!*
> Vivet *in Famâ nunquam moritorus!* [3]

* Doctor Brownrigg's Publications were:

1. An Inaugural Dissertation *"De Praxi Medica ineunda."* Lugduni Batavorum 1737.

2. Essays on Mineral Exhalations [Published in 1741–2.]

3. On the Uses of a Knowledge of Mineral Exhalations, when applied to discover the Principles of Mineral Waters; the Nature of Burning Fountains; and of those poisonous Lakes which the Ancients called *Averni.* [Read before the Royal Society and published in 1741.]

4. An Account of a Laboratory erected near Whitehaven, in 1746: for the Purpose of accurately investigating the Properties of inflammable Air: and for the performance of various Operations in Chemistry.

5. The Art of making Common Salt, as now practiced in most Parts of the World: with several Improvements proposed in that Art: for the Use of the British Dominions. London, 1748. [An Abridgement of this useful Publication, along with the preceding Essays, was inserted in the 45th and 55th Volumes of the Philosophical Transactions of the Royal Society.]

6. A brief Account of the Metal *Platina:* its Origin and Properties [presented to the Royal Society in 1750.]

7. Explanatory Notes to a Poem descriptive of the Coal Works at Whitehaven. [Published by John Dalton, D.D. in 1755 and inserted in Pearch's Oxford Collection]

8. An experimental Inquiry concerning the mineral elastic Spirit, or Air, contained in the waters of Spa in Germany: as well as into the mephitic Qualities of that Spirit. [Philosophical Transactions, Vol. 55th, 1755.]

9. On the means of preventing the Communication of pestilential Contagion, and of eradicating its infected Places. London 1771.

---

3. Translated from the Latin this means,
'Until now he has lived among the good, May his reputation live forever.'

10. Thoughts on the late Rev. Dr. Hales's New Method of Diſtillation, by the united Force of Air and Fire. [Prefixed in a letter to the Rev. Stephen Hales D.D. F.R.S.— it is dated 'Whitehaven, 3 Dec. 1755.' and was read along with the 'Thoughts' before the Royal Society, on the 26th of February 1756.]

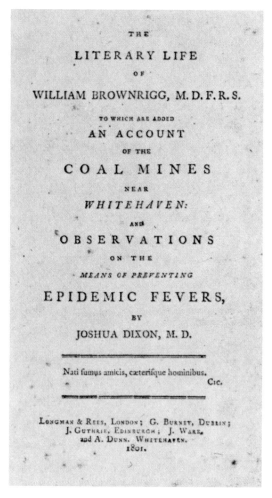

THE

LITERARY LIFE

OF

WILLIAM BROWNRIGG, M.D.F.R.S.

TO WHICH ARE ADDED

AN ACCOUNT

OF THE

COAL MINES

NEAR

WHITEHAVEN:

AND

OBSERVATIONS

ON THE

MEANS OF PREVENTING

EPIDEMIC FEVERS,

BY

JOSHUA DIXON, M.D.

Nati ſumus amicis, cæterifque hominibus.
Cic.

Longman & Rees, London; G. Burnet, Dublin;
J. Guthrie, Edinburgh; J. Ware,
and A. Dunn. Whitehaven.
1801.

TITLE PAGE OF THE LITERARY LIFE OF WILLIAM BROWNRIGG.
Courtesy of Cumbria Records Office and Local Studies Library (Whitehaven).

WHITEHAVEN DISPENSARY

A FEW days ago, as a poor boy by the name of Hewetson was gathering chips under the scaffolding of a new vessel on the blocks in this port, a carpenter's tool box fell upon his head and fractured his skull in so dreadful a manner that a part of the brain protruded. He was immediately taken to the Dispensary under the care of Messrs. Harris and Crosthwaite, Surgeons, and, notwithstanding the magnitude of the fracture, hopes are entertained of his recovery, as he has survived this melancholy accident twelve days. He is only 5 years old. *August* 13th, 1793.

THURSDAY LAST, a lady walking through the New Houses observed a swine chasing a little girl, and snatching at a piece of bread and butter, which she held in her hand. She called out, and the mother of the child coming out of her house at the same time, with difficulty rescued it from the voracious animal.

A correspondent also informs us of a robbery committed on Wednesday by one of these grunting gentry. A little boy had been sent to the green market for a bunch of carrots, which were instantly taken out of his hand by a great fat sow. IT WAS IN VAIN TO CONTEND WITH HER.

THE DANGERS
OF FEELING
THE PULSE

THE conduct of medical practitioners ought, in all cases, to be governed by the strictest rules of prudence; not only as it related to their own safety, but to that of the community. From the attendants they should receive their chief information; and previous to their entrance into the chamber of the sick ought to take a small portion of spirits alone, or impregnated with aromatics; Huxham's tincture of the bark; or a glass of port wine, acidulated with lemon juice, and sweetened with sugar. Some mode of fumigation might, at this time, be practiced; and that of gunpowder, on account of its instantaneous explosion, is deserving of preference. In the room they might chew a small piece of calamus aromaticus, zedoary, angelica, cinnamon, cardamoms, elecampane, ginger, tobacco, or dried lemon peel; observing the precaution of not swallowing the saliva. To prevent the absorption of the contagious matter, it would be proper to dip their fingers in camphorated oil, before they examine the state of the pulse, tongue, and skin; and omitting all

N.B. This entire chapter is an extract of Joshua Dixons writings.

unnecessary inquiries, should remain a very few minutes in the chamber. It is here particularly requisite to remind them of the danger of feeling the pulse of the patient under the bedclothes: this imprudence gave occasion to that disease, which terminated the useful existence of the humane Mr. Howard. After retiring from the apartment, they should immediately wash their hands, rinse their mouth, blow their nose, and, if the contagion is of a very virulent nature, change their clothes as soon as convenient. To the attendants some of these intimations are equally applicable; and should, therefore, be carefully observed by them.

The odours of rue, rosemary, wormwood, sage, lavender, mint, thyme or rose, resist or correct contagious effluvia, and might, therefore, be inhaled, with advantage. The chewing of garlic has been recommended by many eminent Physicians,

PHYSCIAN TAKING THE PULSE OF A FEMALE PATIENT IN BED. Wellcome Library, London.

as a powerful antiseptic. The use of snuff, the chewing or smoking of tobacco, and the application to the nose of sponges dipt in vinegar, in which camphor, rue, wormwood, or rosemary have been infused, would be attended with considerable benefit.

A prudent regulation of jails will promote in a high degree, the salubrity of the adjacent district. To these unhappy abodes, contagious fevers can generally be traced; and here they assume a more malignant aspect. The inferiority of our prisons to those of foreign States, in size, accommodations and management, has cast a shade over the lustre of the British character. It is indeed a disgraceful fact, that the jail fever rarely prevails in other countries; whereas in England, it rages with such violence that, notwithstanding the sanguinary spirit of the laws, the proportion of its victims exceeds that of those who are executed. If the common instincts of humanity, or considerations of interest are insufficient to produce a reformation of the police in this respect; yet it is to be hoped, that a principle of shame, will, at length, excite the general wish of vindicating the national honour from that imputation, which, at present, attaches to it. The frequent appearance of contagion amongst convicts, is chiefly occasioned, by their sudden transition from a nutritive and plentiful, to a poor and scanty diet; by the want of customary exercise, and by the dampness of their habitations. Tortured with the consciousness of guilt, or sinking under the pressure of unmerited obloquy; removed from every friend who might sooth their anguish, by administering consolation and sympathising in their afflictions; recollecting with mixed sensations of horror and regret the irrecoverable hours of innocence and happiness; and surrounded by objects which inspire the mind with gloomy ideas: they possess in the depression of their spirits, a predisposition to the power of contagion. The disease thus meeting with no resistance to its progress, soon pervades the inmoſt recesses of the prison; and not confining itself within the limits of the place, where it was generated, spreads desolation amongſt every order of the community. By a milder treatment of the prisoners, on their firſt admission, by gradually, not suddenly depriving them of their former comforts; by a uniform attention to cleanliness and ventilation; by a regular allowance of fuel, and by preserving their rooms from cold and moiſture; the infeƈtion would either remain dormant, or would readily be extinguished. The politician, who, under the specious pretence of sacrificing to the rigid diƈtates of juſtice the finer feelings of our nature, is, in reality, unsusceptible of the tender emotions of pity, for the miseries of his fellow creatures, will probably rejeƈt such a proposal with ridicule and contempt, as the result of a heated imagination, and an inexperienced judgement. Let us then infliƈt fewer punishments: let us calculate, with accuracy, what degree of bodily pain will counterbalance those indulgences which are to be granted to the prisoners; but let not the innocent members of society become equal sufferers with the guilty.

That infeƈtion may be received even from those who have never suffered the disease has been ascertained from melancholy experience. An additional proof was afforded at the Old Bailey sessions, on the 11th of May, 1750. The contagion was communicated by prisoners apparently free from it; and the Lord Mayor, two of the Judges, one of the Aldermen, two of the Council, one of the Undersherriffs, several of the Middlesex jury, and forty others were deplorable inſtances of its fatality. These events suggeſt the expediency of carefully washing the prisoners, and of dressing them in a clean suit of clothes, previous to their entrance into court. When, on any urgent occasion, a compliance with this direƈtion is impraƈticable; the persons whose presence is requisite, should use the precaution of placing themselves to windward of the prisoner.

The situation of churches, burial places, workhouses, jails and hospitals, should never be in the centre of a large town, since contagion is thus powerfully strengthened and easily disseminated. The internment of a corpse within the precincts of a town was forbidden by the Athenians. It was forbidden also by the Roman law. The danger and indecency of interring bodies, in any part of a church, require an abolition of this long established practice. The corpse of a person, whose death has been the effect of a malignant fever, should, on no occasion, be admitted into a place of public worship; but must be conveyed directly to the grave, where only that part of the service to be read, which immediately relates to its burial: the remaining portion of the office, may be performed, after the interment. The ruinous state of many churches is an insult to the Deity; and is inconsistent with the solemnity of their purpose, to which they are appropriated. Their consequent moisture, also, exposes the congregation to colds and fevers; and deters the piously disposed, from engaging in acts of social prayer. Their preservation, therefore, from damp; and their immediate repairs will be conducive as well to the interests of religion, as to the security of society. The vapour arising from myrhh, frankincense, and particularly juniper berries might, with advantage, be diffused in them, during the prevalence of contagious disease. The odour of the latter can always be perceived in Roman Catholic churches, upon the continent: or wherever a great concourse of people is expected.

From *'Observations on the Means of Preventing Epidemic Fevers.'* Joshua Dixon M.D.

J. Ware and A. Dunn Whitehaven 1801.

DOCTOR GRAHAM
PHYSICIAN *from* EDINBURGH

Desires most respectfully to inform the Ladies and Gentlemen of Whitehaven, and of the adjacent Towns and County, that he feels it to be his Duty to comply with the urgent and repeated Requeſt of a great number of the principal Gentlemen of this Town, and to complete his plan of promoting general Health and Happineſs to his Fellow Creatures in theſe parts of England.

Dr. Graham's Reſidence in Whitehaven will only be about two months. Thoſe perſons afflicted with Diſeaſes that have baffled the Skill of other Doctors, and reſiſted the Power of the moſt celebrated Medicines, ſhould loſe no time in applying to Dr. Graham, that their cures may be confirmed before he leaves this part of the County—an opportunity if not embraced, they will aſsuredly wiſh for in vain, when too late. *July* 30th, 1788

POSTSCRIPT

Yeſterday morning, Dr. James Graham was ſet off to Edinburgh in the cuſtody of two conſtables. This unfortunate man had, for ſome days paſt, diſcovered ſuch marks of infanity, as made it adviſable to ſecure him.

Auguſt 20th, 1788

THE ECONOMICS
OF THE
DISPENSARY

In 1783, the process of collecting subscriptions to finance the initial costs of the Dispensary had received a vital impetus by the donation of £100, by James, Earl of Lonsdale. This donation proved crucial to the solvency of the new venture, as the disbursements accrued in the first year were significantly in excess of the annual subscriptions. There were 115 subscribers in the first Dispensary year, which ran from June 1783 to June 1784. Total subscriptions were £95 15s, while disbursements were £112 19s. Expenses included the costs of setting up the dispensary in the rented house in Scotch-Street. The house required joinery and painting work, and furniture and fixtures had to be provided. The initial outlay on Drugs and Medicines was £34 3s. 8d. The only paid employee of the Dispensary was the apothecary, who had an annual salary of £30. At the first Annual Meeting of the Dispensary, the apothecary was awarded a gratuity of five guineas 'for his close attention to the duties of his office, and in consideration of his having attended, as long as was necessary, so large a number as 1,021 patients at their own habitations'.

Subscribers in that first year included the clergy, Physicians, active and retired, surgeons, druggists and apothecaries, and a wide spectrum of the successful men of the town. Included were members of the Lutwidge and Gale families who had survived bankruptcy after the collapse of the tobacco trade. Subscriptions came from merchants and gentlemen, shipbuilders and sail makers, attorneys, custom officers and tax collectors. Only six subscriptions came from women.

At the conclusion of the first Dispensary year, the Treasurer, Mr. John Gibbon, announced a very satisfactory balance of £93 6s. Encouraged by the initial success of the Dispensary, subscribers in the second year increased to 136, contributing a total of £118 11s 6d. New subscribers included Revd. Gilbert Filkin from Warwickshire, John Doughty, a druggist from Newcastle, and the Friendly Society at the Three Tuns. Additional items of equipment were purchased in 1784, including an electrical machine, and the Humane Society apparatus for the recovery of persons apparently dead from drowning. Subscriptions just exceeded disbursements by £10, but, cushioned by the Earl of Lonsdale's initial benefaction, the Treasurer was able to declare an end of year balance of £103 4s. 5d. £100 of this balance was invested locally and declared in the accounts of the following year as 'Cash Lent'. This accrued an annual interest of £5. Dixon commented that the registered cases presenting to the Dispensary, especially in the surgical department, had greatly increased during the year, and that the 'Trivial Cases' were also more numerous. Despite this, the general disbursements had reduced, so that 'the utility and economy of this Institution may certainly be inferred'. In 1785–86, additional income came from the profits of a benefit play, and from collections following sermons in all the churches of the town. The end of year balance consolidated to £158 10s 1¾d.

Despite increases in the cost of drugs and medicines, which totalled £86 13s 11d in 1786–87, compared to £34 3s 8d in the first year, the Dispensary was financially sound and managed to accumulate a healthy reserve of capital in ensuing years. Subscribers now came from different parts of the country reflecting the trading patterns of the town. Druggists from Leeds, York and Newcastle became annual subscribers. Notable members of the gentry who supported the Dispensary included John Christian Curwen of Workington Hall, Sir Wilfrid Lawson of Brayton, the Fletchers of Hutton Hall and J.T. Senhouse of Calder Abbey. In 1788, Thomas Littledale of Rotterdam, gave a benefaction of £20 to the Dispensary

In the last eight years of the eighteenth century, annual subscriptions fell below £100, reaching a low point of £91 18s 6d in 1799. This corresponded with a period of recession and real poverty in the town. In his report for 1796, Joshua Dixon comments that the Dispensary disbursements regularly exceed the annual subscriptions, which were reduced in number because of the death or penury of regular subscribers. James Hogarth, the donor of 107 Queen Street, died in March 1796. His executors did not prove as charitable, and disbursements in future years again included house rent. In 1798, the death of Anthony Benn, the Dispensary's 'original Promoter and first very munificent subscriber' was a particular challenge. Dixon comments that almost half the original subscribers had by then died, and that others, due to a series of 'misfortunate events, were compelled to withdraw their usual bounties'.

However, the early years of the new century brought fresh financial stability to the Dispensary. This was due, in part, to an increase in new subscribers from Liverpool, Lincolnshire and Jamaica. The main development, however, was the death of James Earl of Lonsdale in 1802. His successor, William Viscount Lowther, announced a benefaction of £50 in 1803, and an annual donation of £10 thereafter. Expenses were of course increasing. In 1803 drugs and medicines amounted to £99 3s 7 ½ , Midwifery costs were £13 7s 6d and the apothecary now earned £51 per annum. Fresh costs included wine and a nurse-keeper for the fever patients.

The year 1807–1808 is representative of this period in the history of the Dispensary. By now, 94,000 persons had been treated at the Dispensary, mostly with the 'combined sufferings of poverty and sickness'. Dixon comments with pride that 'Six years have elapsed since any powerful and alarming Epidemic has prevailed in this town; which previously to the institution of the CHARITY, was visited almost annually by a Fever of the most malignant nature'. Subscriptions of £169 12s 6d comfortably exceed the disbursements of £132 8s 9d. Accumulated cash invested was £510 5s. producing interest of £23 13s 8d. The end of year balance was £577 8s 3d. The Dispensary was flourishing both medically and financially.

B A U M E *d e* V I E

THIS CELEBRATED AND
LONG ESTABLISHED MEDICINE

fortifies the Stomach and Bowels, purifies the Blood
and Juices and gives to the whole Syſtem its natural
equilibrium. To theſe qualities, we attribute its having
being ſo eminently ſerviceable in Gouty, Rheumatic,
Bilious and Scorbutic habits. From the ſame principles,
it has never failed to relieve in Languid, Nervous
and Hypochondriac Caſes, and in Female Diſorders,
it has been found to be particularly beneficial.

JOSHUA DIXON-
THE FIRST
MEDICAL OFFICER
OF HEALTH

Joshua Dixon's main work revolved around the prevention and treatment of the regular epidemics of infectious disease, which devastated Whitehaven. Dixon deserves a reputation as one of the first effective public health Physicians in England. From the beginning, he realised the importance of prevention as the first and most important weapon in the fight against infectious disease. Once an infectious fever occurred, any treatment Dixon was able to offer was merely symptomatic or palliative. The outcome depended on the result of the interaction between the 'contagion' and its host. Often, the victim was already compromised by poverty, overcrowding, a poor diet and the lack of any amenities to support the illness. These are the conditions Dixon tried to improve in the town. He anticipated the post of Medical Officer of Health by one hundred years. In 1790, referring to yet another outbreak of Nervous Fever, he wrote:

The peculiar Circumstances, highly qualified to increase the Power and aggravate the Virulency of Contagion, were the unwholesome food from which the Poor, from the Scarcity of Provisions, unavoidably employed; the putrid Emanations with which the Air in confined Habitations is abundantly impregnated; and the want of Cleanliness in their Persons and Clothing. To these as a more immediate and exciting Cause may be added their incautious, frequent Intercourse with Infected Persons.

The insalubrious State of the Air in the Abodes of the INDIGENT SICK, was corrected and obviated, so far as their situations would admit, by constant complete Ventilation, the immediate removal of the Contaminated Articles (an abundant Source of malignant Effluvia) which were repeatedly immersed in cold water, lest the Vapour excited by Heat, acrimoniously volatilising the poison, should communicate the Distemper. And, as there can be no Mean more conducive to the salutary Purpose of preventing Contagion and preserving Health than that of Cleanliness, a diligent Attention to the Circumstances immediately or remotely connected with it have been everywhere especially inculcated.

The effluvia of Lime, when pulverised by frequent Additions of small Quantities of Water, and the Vapours of Tobacco, Tar and Vinegar, were also copiously employed; with the occasional explosion of Gun-powder, and the various Modes of Fumigation by Sulphur, Juniper Berries, Myrrh, Camphor, Aromatic Herbs, or any other article possessed of pungent and penetrating Odour. Had the Clemency of the Weather permitted, Cold Bathing, particularly to children, would have been useful.

Dixon then recommends to the 'lower class of person', the twice yearly application of whitewash prepared from fresh burnt lime to the scraped walls and ceilings of their houses, as an antidote to infection. He points out that the cost of this is trivial: 'One horse load of lime, price sevenpence halfpenny, is enough to whitewash at least twelve cottages.' The means to avoid the spread of contagious fever are referred to by Dixon as 'our Prophylactics'. He specifies them again in 1798:

As applicable to similar Occasions it may not be improper to here enumerate our principal PROPHYLACTICS.—Cleanliness—

the frequent Change of Bed Cloaths and Linen—the conſtant Admission of fresh Air—the burning of Fuel—recent White Wash—the Evolution of the Nitrous Acid by the Mode formerly directed—the Explosion of Gun-powder, or its Fumigation combined with Vinegar—that of Sulphur, Tobacco, tar, acrid Resins, Frankincense, Juniper Berries, Myrrh, Camphire, and Quick Lime—the pungent yet grateful Odour of aromatic Herbs- the vapour of boiling Vinegar impregnated with Myrrh—Preclude every Intercourse or Connection with infected Persons or Places, and admit the immediate Internment of the Dead in Fever. The Tone of the Syſtem should be supported by the judicious use of the Cold Bath—moderate Labour and warm Cloathings—a generous Diet with ſtimulant Preparations of the Bark and Bitters. The Influence of the Diſtressing Passions, Fear and Grief, to be carefully guarded againſt: Tranquillity, Cheerfulness and Fortitude of Mind being the beſt Preservatives from the Power of Contagion."

Treatment of Contagious Fever began with the use of an emetic and progressed through most of the medicines available at the time, ending with a stimulating draught of wine or port.

In regard to the eligible Treatment of the epidemic Disorder remitted to our Care, we can, from the numerous and well atteſted Facts of Experience, confidently aver, that agreeably to former Observations, the immediate Exhibition of an active EMETIC has, in a great Variety of Inſtances, not only relieved the present febrile Symptoms, but frequently and effectually prevented their future powerful Recurrence. With these Views, it has been generally recommended to Patients of this Discription as the firſt and moſt beneficial Remedy.

ANTIMONIAL PREPARATIONS, sometimes critically promoting a salutary determination to the Surface of the Body, in the early Periods of Disease, would have been certainly injurious in the further Progress of it. Of the ſtimulant SUDORIFICS employed, Serpentaria Decoctions and the Volatile alkali were the chief. OPIATES became requisite whenever a State of Irritability and Inquietude, originating from previous Languor and Relaxation, diſtressfully prevailed; and were for the moſt part highly efficacious. In the terminating Stage of Fever, MOSCH ,and more especially CAMPHOR, united with CARDIACS, in doses of ten or fifteen Grains, taken every two or three hours, sensibly obviating the delirious Tendency, and mitigating the Violence of the spasmodic Contractions, gave, in several Cases, the pleasing Prospect of a certain Recovery; which the regular and abundant Employment of the BARK afterwards perfectly accomplished.

In the DISBURSEMENTS for the past Year, the article of Wine will appear to have been remarkably expensive. Coinciding with our general curative Indications, and the various Remedies qualified to fulfil them, we gratefully acknowledge the humane Interposition of a generous PUBLIC and the LIBERALITY of PRIVATE BENEVOLENCE, enabling us to afford a supply of this most necessary Cordial; which, as it is our Comfort in Time of Health, is also our succour in that of Disease.

Prophylactics recommended in later years included the explosion of gunpowder, and the evolution of nitrous acid. The explosion of gunpowder with 'boles of vinegar' was a technique developed in the Navy, and was designed to prevent the influx of contaminated external air. Nitrous vapour was used to purify the air on hospital wards. In 1796, Dixon recommended the employment of a Nurse-keeper, to ensure the cleanliness of the abodes of the sick, and to carry out the necessary fumigations.

> The mode in which the Nitrous Vapour was raised and applied in the Hospital by Dr. SMITH was by putting Sand, previously heated, into Quart Earthen Pipkins, immersing in each a common Tea Cup containing strong Vitriolic Acid, and as much Nitre in Powder. The Pipkins were carried through the Wards and about the Beds of the Sick; the Bearer constantly stirring the mixture in the Cups with a Glass Spatula. The Fumigation was practised twice in a Day; once only being found insufficient to extinguish the Contagion. If a perpetual Effusion of the Nitrous Vapour is required, the Vessel containing the Nitre and Vitriolic Acid might be placed over a Lamp: the fumigating One invented for the Purpose by Mozer is particularly recommended.
>
> This Expedient, from the Success which attended it, appears to possess a specific Efficacy in decomposing the Principles of

Contagion, and rendering them innoxious. It has lately been found useful in the Fevers of Workhouses and in those originating from Want of Cleanliness in the confined Abodes of the Poor. Armed with this Antidote, we are assured that any Person may safely visit these contaminated Places, and very probably, by this Precaution, save many Lives, without endangering his own.

Joshua Dixon displays a holistic approach to the practice of Medicine, and anticipates many of the 'advances' of our own time. He is acutely aware of the gap in health between the rich and poor, and of the role of poverty, overcrowding and poor sanitation in the evolution of illness. He also gives importance to the role of psychological factors in preserving health and fighting disease, recommending that 'distressing passions' should be replaced by tranquillity and fortitude of mind. Dixon is also sensitive to the special needs of dying patients, and, in 1798, gives a perfect description of palliative care:

> To the extreme Severity of the weather, in the Winter and Spring, might be very probably attributed not only the frequent Recurrence of *chronic* Maladies; but also their violent and perilous Tendency: especially in the Aged, or where previous acute Disease had debilitated the System. *Asthma, Rheumatism, Diarrhoea* and *General weakness*, were of these the chief. To the major Part of such almost irremediable Cases, our Attentions have been merely palliative. Though we could not certainly prevent, it was generally in our Power to retard impending Fatality. Its Approach would then become more gradual and less perceptible; whilst to the remaining Periods of Existence, Moments of transient Relief, and sometimes Intervals of permanent Ease, might be happily procured. If medical care could not, under such deplorable Circumstances, perfectly obstruct it, it was at least enabled to benignly smooth the Avenues of Death, and render its poignant Sufferings in many Respects supportable. For an Operation so beneficial, we are chiefly indebted to the Employment of Opiate Preparations: in Doses proportioned to the Urgency of the then presiding Symptoms: and occasionally repeated, so as to secure or promote their tonic or alleviating Influence.

COMMON
CHILDHOOD INFECTIONS
IN THE
DISPENSARY

ALTHOUGH Joshua Dixon classifies most episodes of contagious disease by the type of fever it evokes, he does recognise some specific infections in the same terms we use today. These include hooping cough (sic), croup, measles, and scarlet fever. Dixon realises that hooping cough is an illness, which is encountered only once in life, but lacking any knowledge of the theory of immunity, he is unable to explain this. Typically, he relates the severity of an epidemic of hooping cough to the state of the weather:

> The HOOPING COUGH, a specific Contagion, which mildly obtained in this Town and Country these nine years, has lately in many instances, assumed every appearance of baneful Virulency: With the lower class of people its Symptoms and event were more benign, less tedious and destructive, than with the Children of the Opulent. EMETICS and a frequent CHANGE of AIR are the best remedies of Experience. A transient Mutation in the state of the latter, especially of moist and warm to dry and cold

weather, being oft observed to sensibly relieve the most alarming Circumstances of Disease. Our Apprehensions with regard to the Prevalency and Danger of this Malady in the Winter, were perfectly removed by the Approach of a favourable Season; and it has not since potently recurred.

In 1797, an epidemic of 184 cases of Hooping Cough occurred, with only two fatalities:

The epidemic Affections to which the Children of the Indigent had been liable, in the Course of the Winter and Spring, still continued to obtain: of these the *Hooping Cough* was the most frequent and powerful. Amongst the lower Classes of People, where little Regard could be paid to the proper Government of the Regimen, (especially it's principal Articles of Air and Diet) this Contagion raged with peculiar Violence. Repeated *Emetics*, topical *Blood-letting*, with the occasional application of *Blisters*, were chiefly relied upon. Their Efficacy, in sensibly alleviating the Urgency of present Symptoms, and sometimes preventing any expected dangerous Attack were always observable. In the last Stage of the Disease, when an inflammatory Tendency no longer prevailed, vegetable and mineral Tonics with Antispasmodics and external Stimulants, became manifestly useful. It must be acknowledged that in a Malady not less tedious and painful to its Objects, than alarming to their relative Connections, very permanent Advantage has been derived, exclusive of medical Aid, from varying the Mode of Living of the Patient, particularly permitting a total Change of Air, or rather, in mild and temperate Weather, a long continued Stream of it. In this Disease, 184 Patients have been attended to, and though several long suffered very distressful Symptoms, two only were fatal Cases. Families residing in convenient situations, are said to find its most urgent symptoms sensibly mitigated, by taking the children down into the coalmines.

Much more serious in terms of mortality, were the winter epidemics of croup. Similar epidemics usually due to Para influenza virus type b still occur. Croup remains an alarming experience and can be life threatening. A variety of treatments were in use in 1811, including leeches, and the application of blisters to the throat. Dixon points out that early treatment of the initially mild symptoms is vital.

No disease has proved so fatal to Children as the CROUP, especially when, from the mild and deceitful nature of the primary symptoms, medical advice was not solicited till its advanced and nearly closing period. General and *topical blood-letting*, the application of *blisters* to the throat, the active operation of *emetics*, with *volatile fetids* and *purgatives*, were the usual palliative expedients, but which rarely effected a cure. The modern practice of PUBLIC ESTABLISHMENTS, sanctioned by the highest authority, has recommended, in any stage of its progress, the immediate, repeated and liberal exhibition of *Calomel*, as the only medicine, which, superseding the necessity of any other, affords a prospect of recovery, or even of transient relief, in this deplorable malady.- The experience of the DISPENSARY, with regard to the use of *Mercury*, which may be deemed the *anceps remedium potius quam nullum*[4], in this disease, has been limited to a very few cases. We shall notice three, which have occurred within the last three years. In the first, a child, aged 2½ years, the immense quantity of thirty-six grains of *Calomel* was directed to be taken, in the space of three days, yet, excepting its affording a temporary mitigation to the urgency of the principal symptoms, no other sensible effects could be discovered. The second case was that of a healthy child, 3½ years old, in which the usual symptoms of languor, insensibility, convulsive contractions, and peculiar difficulty in breathing, requiring the exertion of every muscle connected with respiration, were remarkably powerful. From the operations of an *emetic* and a *purgative* she derived no benefit. The application of leeches and that of a *blister* to the throat, were equally inefficacious. The mercurial course commenced on the second day of the disease, and the child took two grains of *Calomel* every two hours, till a moderate degree of salivation was excited; and afterwards, by reduced doses, gradually promoted: the whole quantity taken exceeding fifteen grains. By this means, the patient experienced considerable relief, and in three days was restored to perfect health. In the third instance, a child, aged three years, suffered the singular and violent symptoms of the *Croup*. Immediate application being made to the DISPENSARY, its recovery was, happily, effected in the space of one day. An emetic was prescribed, a *blister* applied to the throat, and twelve grains of *Calomel* were taken, in a dose of three grains every three hours.

Mr. JAMES ANDERSON, an experienced surgeon in *Edinburgh*, highly approves the use of *Mercury*, in this disease. He has given to a child, aged three years, in whom the symptoms were urgent, eighteen grains of *Calomel*, in twenty-four hours, in doses of two or three grains every hour. In no case has the medicine produced any violent evacuation, or excited any painful irritation of the bowels. Several professional Gentlemen of eminence, in this country, have pursued the same mode of practice, judiciously varied by the state of circumstances, with considerable success.

Joshua Dixon's approach to the treatment of croup demonstrates the comprehensive nature of his practice, and his willingness to adopt the modern management of the time. He is aware of advances in treatment pioneered in the university centres of England and Scotland.

Epidemics of measles occurred in Whitehaven with a periodicity of three to seven years. Measles, like smallpox and chickenpox, is extremely infectious, and will generally infect all susceptible children in a community. Following an epidemic, the current cohort of children would be immune. The next epidemic would require a new cohort of vulnerable children, and an infecting case of measles from another community. In Joshua Dixon's times, because of the infrequency of travel, it was usually possible to trace the source of the infection. An epidemic of measles occurred in 1793, after seven years of freedom from the disease:

To the acute, epidemic Diseases of Children, as remarkably prevalent, our Attention has been principally directed. Sincerely do we deplore their Fatality, and the disregard of parents in preventing it. The first and most interesting was the Measles: a Contagion, which had not obtained here, these seven Years. Two Children were unexpectedly seized with it in the month of June: The Symptoms of the Younger required no particular Assistance; but those of the Eldest became very active and dangerous. Accurately tracing the Source of this Disease, we found the Family had lately removed from *Carlisle*, where it then generally and potently raged. The warm and temperate State of the Weather, during the Summer and Autumn, happily rendered this destructive Malady of Children singularly favourable, and effectually promoted every curative Expedient: not One of 262 Cases suffering a fatal Termination. In those Patients who, a little advanced in life, were consequently liable to more acute and alarming pulmonic Symptoms, a Recovery, though finally perfect, was, with Difficulty, tediously accomplished. The principal Medical Regards, under such Circumstances, have been chiefly confined to obviate the general Tendency to Inflammation, and especially that powerful determination to the Lungs, which peculiarly characterising the Disease, always occasions it's Uncertainty and Danger. With these Views, repeated large Blood-lettings, and the Application of Blisters were, when the Symptoms became violent, remarkably beneficial. SALINE and AINTIMONIAL Preparations have been prescribed with considerable Efficacy, wherever a febrile Tendency gave the Indication; and mucilaginous Pectorals to mitigate the frequent, very troublesome catarrhal Irritations. The Regimen of the Sick was also, with the greatest Utility, strictly governed. Diluent and demulcent Articles liberally administered, and a State of Moderate and equable Perspiration, by Means the least stimulant, generally promoted; the exciting Influence of Cold being cautiously guarded against.

Scarlet fever is a specific form of tonsillitis, caused by a haemolytic streptococcus, which produces an 'erythrogenic toxin', causing the typical rash. In addition the illness is characterised by a 'strawberry tongue'. Common features also include ear infections and enlargement of the lymphatic glands of the neck. Dixon's description of the illness in 1794 is comprehensive.

The SCARLET FEVER, which had not generally raged here since the Spring of 1788, was the chief Epidemic of this Year. The Origin of a Disease so singularly destructive to Children could not be precisely determined. We only find that it first made its Appearance in the Summer, gradually acquiring and diffusing a very malignant Influence during the Whole of the Autumn, and till the Beginning of Winter. The mild and moist State of these Seasons, especially in *November* and Part of *December*, induced a putrid, highly pernicious Tendency, which the succeeding keen and permanent frost alone repressed. The Disease then became more favourable; its baneful Prevalency being sensibly interrupted, was soon after finally overcome. Young Subjects and Females of delicate Constitutions, particularly if their general Health had been previously impaired and debilitated by constant Attendance or exquisite Anxiety, were most likely to suffer its powerful and fatal Influence.—Of the Nature and Degree of the Symptoms a considerable Variety in different Patients and Periods, frequently occurred. The principal and most alarming were an unremitting febrile Tendency, with small fluid Eruptions occupying the Surface of the Body; a tumified and ulcerated State of the Throat; thick, livid Incrustations upon the Mouth, Tongue and Lips, with copious Effusions from the Eyes and Nostrils; violent Delerium and ungovernable Restlessness and Inquietude; frequent Nausea, Vomiting, or Diarrhoea; and the whole Concourse accompanied with extreme universal Languor, remarkably obvious in the expression of the Eye. The Duration of this Malady was from three to seven Days; and an irritating separation of the Scars on the Skin; glandular Tumours, especially of the Neck; Deafness arising from Suppurations in the Ear; and oedematous Affections of the Extremities are its frequent Terminations. With Regard to the medical Conduct, as inflammatory Appearances, even in the early Stages of the Disorder, never powerfully obtained, the antiphlogistic Regimen was seldom strictly enjoined, except in cold Seasons and plethoric Habits: On the contrary, its putrecent Disposition, preceded and distinguished by Relaxation and Debility, solely indicated the liberal Employment of Tonics and Antiseptics: Of these, the Bark, Wine, and Mineral Acids with Opiates were most eligible. Blisters to the Throat and detergent Gargles became also occasional palliative Expedients. The Efficacy of the above remedies, in alleviating and removing urgent Symptoms, has been lately so incontestably proved by Experience, that it is highly probable the future Fatality of this Contagion, in Circumstances unpropitiously septic, may, from their copious administration, in many Instances, be certainly anticipated and prevented.

Joshua Dixon stressed the importance of a vigorous approach to the diseases of children as they constitute the 'rising generation' on which the future of the town depends. In 1811, he outlined his principles of paediatric care. An interesting concept is his observation that vomiting is a symptom of most childhood illnesses. Dixon concludes that vomiting is nature's way of ridding the body of toxins, so an emetic is always his first treatment of choice:

> Not less frequent than important, are the *Diseases of Children*, and their causes, nature and effects have been investigated by the most sagacious of Physicians. A few practical observations respecting them may be, here, not improperly introduced; the preservation of the health of the rising generation, upon which depend the future and best interests of the community being justly accounted of the greatest consequence.
>
> To the irritation occasioned by the acrimony of the acid, bilious and viscid fluids, so predominant in the stomach and bowels of Young Children, can be attributed a considerable proportion of the numerous train of disorders, which they frequently suffer. NATURE, benign and provident in all her works, endeavours under such circumstances, to prevent danger, and relieve any urgent complaint, by spontaneous vomiting: and when there is the least variation from the healthy state, the aids of art can never prove more useful than by the attempt, in this regard, to imitate her operations. With these views, *emetics* have been recommended, by judicious and eminent practitioners, as universal remedies, in the diseases of children.
>
> From the experience of DR. CLARKE, of *Dublin,* and that of several celebrated Physicians, whose practice has been particularly directed to the disorders of infants, it appears, that speedy relief, and permanent benefit, may be derived from small doses of *Calomel.* No difficulty attends its exhibition; and it is peculiarly calculated not only to evacuate the contents of the bowels, but also to correct and rectify that state, upon which their acrimony depends.-The occasional use of this medicine will prove highly requisite in those convulsive and spasmodic fits of children, which very often arise from the acrid quality of the fluids, in the intestinal canal.
>
> Children are, also, very liable to a variety of eruptions upon the skin, and no expedient has been adopted more effectual for their removal and prevention than this remedy. Where there is a manifest tendency to costiveness, this preparation of *Mercury* may be accounted the best laxative we can employ. Infants, from two to six months old. may take one third, or half of a grain, at bed-time; and the propriety of repeating the dose must depend

upon the effects produced. *Magnesia alba,* or *rhubarb*, with *ginger*, or *castor oil*, with *syrup*, as operating mildly, and certainly, may prove a useful substitute for this more active remedy, whenever an habitual state of constipation prevails.

The symptoms of *general fever,* excited by the cold, or those of an inflammatory determination to the lungs, sensibly affecting respiration, always indicate the necessity of copious *blood-letting*; the applications of *leeches* and *blisters*; with *saline antimonial*, and opening medicines. The sedative power of the *Digitalis*, taken in substance, or in its best preparation, the *saturated tincture*, has been found remarkably efficacious in such cases.

There is a curious anomaly in the Annual Dispensary Reports of childhood illness. Chicken pox was never recorded in Whitehaven. Dixon is not alone in this respect, as the reports from the Dispensary in Carlisle do not include chicken pox, and the larger Newcastle Dispensary records only one case in its first seven years, and only sporadic cases thereafter. Chicken pox had been recognised since biblical times, and was described in detail in 1776, by the great English Physician, Heberden, who noted the differences between chicken pox and smallpox. It is very unlikely that Dixon and his colleagues in other Dispensaries would all confuse chicken pox with smallpox. The likely explanation seems to be that at this time, chickenpox was absent from the North of England.

D R.   P A T E R S O N.

DR. PATERSON, who lately performed a great number of uncommon cures in Newcaſtle-on-Tyne, may now be conſulted on all Phyſical and Chiurgical Caſes every day in the week [Sundays excepted] from ten-o-clock in the morning till four in the afternoon, at Mrs. Jackſon's, Quay St., where all perſons will be made extremely welcome to hiſ advice, gratis.

He removes Cataracts and Obſtructions of the Optic Nerves. He has reſtored Numbers of People to ſight who have been blind many years.

Numbers afflicted with Deafneſs have been brought to their perfect hearing by him. He cures Pains and Dizzineſs of the Head, Convulſions and Hyſteric Fits, Inward Weakneſs, Low Spritedneſs and all Nervous Debilities.

Alſo Aſthma, Coughs, Conſumptions and Windy Complaints, and all Diſorders in Stomachs and Bowels. He cures the Dropſy, Leproſy, Scurvy, Scald Head, Rheumatiſm and Jaundice, alſo the Gravel and all ſtony concretions formed in the Kidneys or Bladder. He cures Cancers, King's Evil. Wens and Ulcerated legs, alſo Fiſtulas and Piles and the Venereal Diſeaſe in all its ſtages.

☞ N.B. HE CURES THE ABOVE DISORDERS BY MEDICINES PREPARED FROM VEGETABLES.

EDWARD JENNER
AND THE
WHITEHAVEN DISPENSARY

As the eighteenth century ended, enthusiasm for smallpox inoculation had tempered. Although it was clear that a successful inoculation did protect from a future attack of smallpox, doubts remained over its safety. An observation made in 1796, by a Gloucester Physician, Edward Jenner, changed the whole approach to the prevention of smallpox, although not without fresh controversy.

Edward Jenner was born in Berkeley, Glouccstershire, in 1749, the third son of the local vicar. Jenner left school at the age of thirteen, and was apprenticed to a surgeon-apothecary, Daniel Ludlow, of Sodbury, near Bristol. In 1770, he travelled to London, where he spent two years as resident apprentice to the celebrated surgeon John Hunter, with whom he developed a strong friendship, and professional relationship. He returned to practice in Berkeley in 1772. Jenner's interests included natural history, as well as medicine. In 1788, he was elected to the Fellowship of the Royal Society, for his paper on the 'Natural History of the

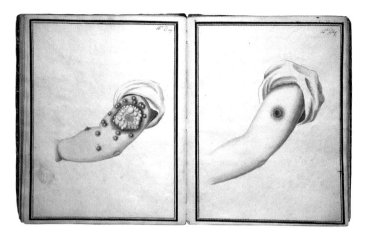

SMALLPOX (LEFT) AND COWPOX INOCULATION, DAY 10.
Wellcome Library, London.

Cuckoo.' In 1792, he obtained the degree of M.D. from St. Andrews, on the recommendation of two colleagues, and the payment of a fee of £30. Jenner settled down to life as a country Physician.

It had long been country lore in Gloucestershire, and other dairy counties, that those who had been infected with cowpox, an eruption that occurred on the udders of cows, were afterwards seemingly protected from smallpox during an epidemic. It also proved impossible to perform a successful inoculation with smallpox, on a person who had previously had cowpox. Jenner observed this latter fact himself on several of his own patients, and decided to try giving cowpox matter artificially as an inoculation, to see if this would protect against smallpox. Cowpox was present on a farm near Berkeley in May 1796, and a dairymaid, named Sarah Nelmes, became infected. On May 14, Jenner took fluid material from a lesion on her hand and inoculated it into the arm of the son of his gardener, an eight-year-old boy called James Phipps. Six weeks later, he inoculated the boy with smallpox in several places. There was no reaction. Jenner concluded that inoculation with cowpox protected against a future infection with smallpox.

Edward Jenner's paper to the Royal Society, presenting this case, was refused as being too contentious. He collected other cases to support his theory and published this himself in a booklet, in 1798, on the 'Causes and Effects of Cowpox'. Initial reaction from the medical profession was hostile. The concept of preventing one disease by giving another was not a scientific possibility in the currency of the day. What was needed was a luminary with a reputation. This arrived in the shape of Dr. George Pearson, Fellow of the Royal College of Physicians and Physician to St. George's Hospital. He collected data over a six-month period and wrote an influential pamphlet recommending the new procedure. Dr. William Woodville, of the Smallpox Inoculation Hospital was the next influential Physician to take up cowpox inoculation, and by July 1800, he had published reports on over 2,000 cases. Jenner himself, in his paper of March 1801, on the 'Origin of Vaccine Inoculation,' claimed that, by then, over 100,000 persons had been inoculated in England alone. The procedure became known as Vaccination, after *vaccus*, the Latin term for 'cow'.

It is tempting to speculate how medical advances reached an isolated town like Whitehaven at the start of the nineteenth century. The town had prospered by developing maritime communications, but had suffered because of its relative landward isolation. Other similar towns may have waited years to receive the benefit of scientific advances, but, in Joshua Dixon, Whitehaven had a man at the head of his field of expertise. Dixon was a prolific writer of tracts and letters. His practice was informed by regular communication with Physicians in London, Edinburgh and Liverpool. For example, Dixon's management of croup utilises the research of the Edinburgh surgeon, James Anderson. His advocacy of cold bathing in fevers is based on the work of Dr. Currie in Liverpool. Dixon was elected to the Medical Society of London in 1789, and established an enduring friendship with a former President of the Society, John Coakley Lettsom, who was an influential figure in London medicine, and in the Dispensary movement. The two men corresponded regularly, and Dixon would have had access to the minutes of the Medical Society meetings.

The Dispensary Annual Report of 1800 shows that Dixon was still using the old method of smallpox inoculation as he reports that 126 children were 'prepared for the smallpox' and 90 were subsequently inoculated. These inoculations took place in the context of an epidemic of 120 cases of smallpox with 11 deaths. By 1801, however, Joshua Dixon is able to write a clear comprehensive exposition of cowpox vaccination, with the advantages it confers, and the refinements of the technique. This Annual Report resembles a teaching reference for other practitioners. He is able to quote the opinions of 'Drs. Woodville, Pearson and Lettsom' in support of vaccination. In 1802, only three smallpox inoculations were performed, with eight cowpox vaccinations taking place later in the year. In 1803, when smallpox was absent from the town, thirty cowpox vaccinations were administered. By 1808, this number had risen to 298. It is a salutary reflection, that only four years after the publication of Jenner's booklet on vaccination, not only do we find the method in regular use in Whitehaven Dispensary, but also that Joshua Dixon has become an expert in the theory and practice of vaccination. This is good evidence of the innovative policies of the Dispensary and illustrates that it was at the forefront of medical practice of the time.

In the spring of 1809, smallpox again became established in the town. The source of the infection was unknown. There were 254 cases of a smallpox of 'remarkable malignancy' and 25 deaths. Meanwhile, cowpox vaccination increased to 451. Over the next seven years, smallpox disappeared from the town, and almost 2,000 people, mainly young children, were vaccinated. In his Annual Report of 1814, Joshua Dixon asserts that 'Whitehaven can join its testimony to that of Norwich, that not a single instance of smallpox has occurred since the adoption of vaccination.' The Annual Report of 1815 contains a summary of the successes and frustrations of Dixon's current practice:

> To the rising Generation of this District the cow-pox INOCULATION hitherto has proved and most assuredly will continue, to be an inestimable Blessing, In order to secure a constant and regular supply of genuine Matter, and to prevent a total privation of it, two or more children are reserved for *Inoculation* the succeeding week, and in large families, the children receive the infection, by inoculation, from each other. Another established rule in the Vaccine Department of this CHARITY is, that of directing the inoculated children to be brought to the Dispensary upon the 4th or 5th day of the disease, and invariably upon the 8th; for the purposes of observing its progressively inflammatory and suppurative symptoms; thereby determining the certainty of its effectual communication. The opportunity then afforded of transmitting the infection to persons requiring it, and of obtaining the same salutary consequence of resisting, in future, the variolous contagion, was an additional inducement for this, in many respects, very necessary injunction.
>
> The utility of these measures, however, frequently was frustrated by the perversity and disobedience of the parents of the inoculated children: and as the precautions, strictly observed, of preventing the introduction of the Natural Small Pox, have been completely successful, and, in consequence, the disease has not prevailed since the year 1808, the lower class of people, not entertaining any apprehensions of it, are less disposed to solicit or admit this most secure antidote to that dreadfully fatal contagion. Many, also, are prejudiced against it, by an absurd and groundless opinion, that every disease, and particularly of the eyes, or if distinguished by tumours, or eruptions, which children may afterwards suffer, is occasioned by its baneful influence upon their constitutions.

To these causes may be attributed the considerable reduction in the number of inoculated patients, when compared with former annual admissions.

This was the essential dilemma facing Dixon during the lifetime of the Dispensary. In the absence of refrigeration, Dixon relied on a continual turnover of children for the supply of cowpox vaccination, in effect using the children vaccinated one week for the next week's supply of vaccine. If parents failed to keep their children's follow up appointments, the vital human chain of cowpox vaccine was broken. The main aim of the Dispensary was to provide free medical care to the industrious poor, who would have an employer or other contact to 'recommend' them to the Dispensary. Implicit in this arrangement is the assumption that the labourer would return to useful work after his illness. Yet below this honest labouring class existed a

EDWARD JENNER VACCINATING A BOY. *Oil Painting by E.E.Hillemacher 1884*
Wellcome Library, London.

community of truly deprived persons, living in overcrowded tenements and damp cellars with little food or warmth, and no personal resources to access aid from the Dispensary. This made them very vulnerable to any infectious disease and despite the relative success of vaccination, there continued to be a vulnerable population in the town. Whitehaven suffered another smallpox epidemic in 1817–1818 with 310 cases, but this turned out to be a mild epidemic with only four deaths. The last three years of Dixon's work in the Dispensary were free of smallpox. Almost 6,000 patients, mainly children, had received cowpox vaccination in the Dispensary. In the twenty years preceding the introduction of cowpox vaccination, there were 152 deaths from smallpox in the Dispensary. Following the adoption of vaccination, deaths from smallpox over the following twenty years reduced to twenty-five.

WHITEHAVEN DISPENSARY

THE General Anniverſary meeting of the PRESIDENTS and GOVERNORS of this Charity will be held at the Diſpenſary in Queen St. on Monday 14th June next, exaĉtly at Twelve-o-Clock. The Gentlemen of the Committee are requeſted to attend a little before that hour.

☞ An APOTHECARY to the Charity will be this day eleĉted.

PETER HOW YOUNGER , Secretary.

May 19th 1790

SCURVY, SCROFULA
AND
SYPHILIS

THE legacy of Joshua Dixon is unique. During his forty years as Physician to the Dispensary, he carefully recorded all the incidents of diseases he encountered, together with their outcomes. The diseases of the first three years are recorded in a simple list form. In subsequent years, Dixon used a tabular system of recording, 'agreeably to the ingenious system of the celebrated Dr. Cullen.' The tables contain a mass of detail, and are a comprehensive summary of the work of Whitehaven Dispensary, as well as giving a remarkable insight into the diseases of the time.

Joshua Dixon's Annual Reports concern themselves almost exclusively with contagious disease. Thus, epidemics of whooping cough, measles, croup, scarlet fever, and particularly smallpox are described and analysed in detail. Dixon makes a particular study of Nervous Fever, collecting all the cases of this fever over forty years and presenting his results in a cumulative tabular form each year. Diseases of a non-infectious nature get scant mention in the Reports, with passing references only to asthma, rheumatism, dropsy and catarrhal illnesses. The reason for this is not difficult to elucidate.

The reputation of the eighteenth-century Physician depended entirely on his ability to 'cure' illness. Joshua Dixon, in common with other Physicians of the time, would regard the resolution of a simple self-limiting illness in his patient as a cure. If the outcome of a potentially fatal disease, such as smallpox, was favourable, then this would be a 'cure' of even greater import. Dixon concentrates his attentions on Infectious Disease, as most cases did get better. This approach is reflected in the end of year figures of the Dispensary, the 'State of the Registers'. 1807–1808 is a typical year:

An ACCOUNT of the PATIENTS
admitted from *June* 8, 1807 to *June* 13, 1808.

Recommended and Regiftered, (of whom 484 were vifited in
their own Houfes)   •   •   1156

Trivial Cafes   •   •   •   2719

Children inoculated for the Cow-Pox   •   •   298

—————

4173

Patients remaining upon the Books, June 8, 1807.   52

—————

4225

THE STATE OF THE REGISTERS

Cured	•	•	•	1340
Relieved	•	•	•	40
Incurable	•	•	•	12
Dead	•	•	•	46
Remaining upon the Books		•	•	68
				1506

Cases summarised in the State of the Registers exclude the Trivial Cases. The deaths recorded correspond to a Standardised Mortality Ratio of thirty deaths per 1,000 patients per year. We know that the Standardised Mortality Ratio in the general population at that time was about forty-five per 1,000 per year. We have to deal therefore, with the curious fact, which pertains every year, that the mortality in Dispensary patients, who are, by definition ill, is significantly less than in the general population. Dixon classifies ninety per cent of his patients in this typical year as 'cured'. Even accepting the natural resolution of an infection, such as measles, as a 'cure', this still means that a large number of chronic illnesses listed in the annual classification of diseases, are regarded as 'cures'. Examples are dropsy, epilepsy, indigestion, flatulency, chronic weakness, rickets, jaundice, dimness of sight, asthma, colic and rheumatism; all but ten per cent are cured. Similar rates of cure are also claimed by Dixon's contemporary in Carlisle Dispensary, the 'Physician Extraordinary', John Heysham. It seems likely that all treated cases, who do not die, are regarded as cures, apart from the small number classified as 'Relieved' or 'Incurable'. A further conundrum arises with midwifery cases. The Annual Report for 1786 describes sixty-five pregnant women 'admitted for delivery'. Total Midwifery admissions during the life of the Dispensary number 1,955. Maternal mortality at that time was at least fifty per 1,000 live births, with deaths mainly occurring from haemorrhage and puerperal fever. Dixon reports no cases of puerperal fever, and only two maternal deaths in the 832 midwifery cases between 1786 and 1792.

In addition to treating the recommended cases, the Dispensary also performed a vital Public Health function for the town. Potentially fatal epidemics of 'contagion' were vigorously defended by quarantine, in which the police, magistrates and port authorities played a part; by smallpox vaccination and by the various prophylactics described in the reports. Dixon declared the town of Whitehaven as being 'free from contagion' whenever he could. By presenting a favourable set of reports each year, Dixon was able to attract continuing subscriptions into the Dispensary and ensure its viability.

In most years, the most common of the non-infectious illnesses recorded in the Dispensary, is scurvy. About 200 cases of 'scorbutic eruptions' were dealt with in Whitehaven each year. This contrasts with the Dispensary in Carlisle, where John Heysham, presents no cases of scurvy, and with the Dispensary in Newcastle, where only sporadic cases are recorded. Scurvy is a disease resulting from vitamin C deficiency, caused by a diet deficient in fresh fruit and vegetables. Vitamin C is necessary for the formation of collagen, which provides structural strength to tissues and the walls of blood vessels. In scurvy, the weakened capillary vessels bleed into the skin and mucous membranes causing haemorrhage into the skin, hair follicles, mouth and intestines. Scurvy was classically a disease of sailors, whose supply of fresh food would run out at an early stage of the voyage, exposing them to vitamin C deficiency. The high prevalence of scurvy in Whitehaven reflects the long voyages made across the Atlantic by the ships of the town. Carlisle had no maritime connections, and, according to Heysham, the diet of the inhabitants of Carlisle was healthy. Although Newcastle-on-Tyne was a busy port, its commerce was with other British ports and Europe, so the ship's crews were not exposed to the health risks of transatlantic crossings. In Whitehaven, Sea Captains, Mariners and their apprentices were specifically excluded from attending the Dispensary, and were expected to obtain medical advice privately from the Physicians of the town. Paupers, or ordinary seamen, hired as cheap labour for the duration of the voyage, and then discarded, would present their scorbutic rash to the Dispensary. Cases of scurvy in Whitehaven also included the poor of the town who had an appalling diet. Dixon does comment in some years on the abundant autumn harvest of fruits and berries, but it seems very unlikely that the poor had access to this source of vitamin C. On the evidence of his detailed Annual Reports, it appears that Joshua Dixon was unaware of any treatment for scurvy.

In 1753, thirty years before the opening of Whitehaven Dispensary, James Lind, a surgeon in the British navy had published his treatise on scurvy. This included one of the first ever recorded clinical trials, carried out on H.M.S. Salisbury, which proved that lemon and orange juice was an effective treatment for scurvy. Unfortunately, the significance of this observation was lost, even to Lind himself, in the other details of the treatise. It was another forty years before lemon juice was added to the naval diet, and even then, this innovation did not immediately become part of medical practice. Although Dixon recognises and records scurvy, he does not write about it in his Annual Reports. He did have competition. Mr. Spillbury's Antiscorbutic Drops, from Soho Square in London, were heavily advertised. Not only did the Drops cure scurvy and gout, they were effective in rheumatism, fistula, consumption and slow fever, and could be obtained from Ware's Printing Office in Whitehaven.

The surgical department of the Dispensary dealt with 'Luxations, fractures and sprains; ulcers and abscesses; contusions wounds and burns'. In addition, most of the smallpox inoculations (and later the cowpox vaccinations) were performed by the surgeons. Dixon comments frequently in his reports of the constant danger faced by the working labourers of the town in their daily work. The *Cumberland Pacquet* carried weekly reports of accidents incurred by sailors, miners, and the ordinary townsfolk in their daily business. Sailors were killed by falls from the masts, or by drowning, and passers-by were in danger from falling tackle from ships. Accidents in the mines were common and often fatal. Children were regularly burnt or scalded in their cramped houses where heating and cooking relied on an open fire. Surgical treatment was basic. Fractures, badly set, would heal slowly. Abscesses were incised. Infected wounds would fester for months. After a major accident, there was nothing but opium and hope.

The surgeons may also have been called upon to deal with the Scrofula, or the King's Evil. This was a gross swelling of the lymph glands of the neck, usually in children, producing an alarming appearance. The cause was a Mycobacterium infection, sometimes the classical M. tuberculosis, or more often an atypical Mycobacterium. In the Middle Ages, it was a common superstition that the King could cure scrofula by touch, hence the popular name.

Childhood fevers and Infectious fevers are the subject of many pages in the Annual Reports, and in other chapters. Some fevers attract little 'official comment'. Worm fever was a common illness in Dispensary patients and confirms that life in eighteenth-century Whitehaven was similar to that in a developing country today, where worm infestation remains common. Infection with tapeworms, long worms and short worms occurred by eating inadequately cooked meats contaminated with worm larvae. Fever and a variety of abdominal and anal symptoms resulted. Diagnosis was made by observing worm segments in the stools. Treatment was with purges containing high amounts of mercury or lead.

Infections of the respiratory tract were common presentations to the Dispensary. Tonsillitis is described as 'Inflammatory Sore Throat', while chest infections or pneumonia is classified as 'Inflammation of the Lungs'. Pulmonary tuberculosis, or consumption, was also common. This is a disease associated with overcrowding, poverty and deprivation, which often has a fatal outcome. In later years, cases of consumption were admitted to the House of Recovery. Treatment of pneumonia or consumption was, of course, symptomatic or palliative, with bleeding, purges, emetics and opium in one of its guises.

Gastrointestinal problems were rife in Dixon's patients. The diet of the poor of Whitehaven was based on bread, barley and sometimes potatoes with little meat or fresh vegetables. Gastric upsets from rotten food were common. Cases of stomach complaints and flatulency presented frequently to the Dispensary. Colic, cholera morbus, diarrhoea and dysentery were part of daily life. Dixon uses these terms in a descriptive way, and not as a pathological diagnosis. Although he uses the term 'cholera' frequently, epidemic cholera caused by *vibrio cholerae* did not reach Whitehaven until the second great cholera pandemic of 1832.

Few cases of mental illness are recorded in the Dispensary. The daily physical challenge of living, eating and keeping warm and safe, was the main priority of the poor of the town. Very few succumbed to melancholy, the classic description of depression of the time. Melancholy and hysteria were afflictions of the eighteenth century well-to-do, and found no place in the Whitehaven Dispensary. More interesting is the substantial group of patients with chronic weakness. Myalgic encephalomyelitis (M.E.) was first described in 1934. Could this be the eighteenth-century equivalent? Or could these patients have some sort of anaemia, a diagnosis surprisingly never made by Dixon?

A common chronic disease of the Dispensary was dropsy. This referred to the accumulation of fluid in any body cavity. Brain dropsy was hydrocephalus, abdominal dropsy was ascites, and cardiac dropsy was the accumulation of fluid in the lungs, pleural spaces, and legs, from heart failure. William Withering, in 1785, had developed the drug digitalis from the foxglove and showed that it was effective in heart failure. Joshua Dixon uses digitalis in the management of scarlet fever.

Rickets was a disease that frequently affected children of the poor in Whitehaven. Known as the English Disease, it was first described in the slums of the industrial revolution. Rickets develops due to deficiency of vitamin D and is caused by a poor diet and lack of exposure to sunlight. It affects children disadvantaged by over crowding and poverty. Rickets causes swelling of the bones, especially of the skull, ribs and spine. In the twentieth century, rickets was almost entirely eradicated by giving children daily supplements of cod liver oil.

Sexually transmitted diseases were uncommon in Dispensary patients. Dixon describes Syphilis as *Lues Venerea*, the plague of Venus. Syphilis appeared at the end of the fifteenth century in France, and had become epidemic by the mid-sixteenth century. In the late eighteenth century, it was often confused with gonorrhoea. The famous English surgeon John Hunter tried to clarify matters by infecting himself with pus from a patient with gonorrhoea. Hunter developed both gonorrhoea and syphilis, as, unknown to him, the patient also had latent syphilis. Syphilis attracted many different remedies from quacks and irregular practitioners. The standard medical treatment of the time was *unguentumm sarasenicum*, which contained mercury. It was applied as an ointment and used in vapour baths.

Incisional surgery was rarely undertaken in the Dispensary, as there was no effective anaesthesia, apart from opium and alcohol, and the outcome was so uncertain, with blood loss and postoperative infections a major risk. An exception was the celebrated operation on the popliteal artery aneurysm, by Surgeon Extraordinary, John Hamilton, described in the Annual Reports. Amputations for gangrene or major accidents were blood-curdling affairs. One of the most common surgical presentations was that of bladder stones, described as 'gravel'. These were removed by the suprapubic route, or via the penis. In London, the surgeon William Cheselden could remove a bladder stone, without anaesthetic, in under five minutes. His fee was £500, payable in advance. Surgical practice in the Whitehaven Dispensary, however, was rather more prosaic. Burns, wounds, abscesses, sprains and subluxations were the order of the day.

THE FINAL YEARS

OF

WHITEHAVEN DISPENSARY

As the nineteeth century progressed, Whitehaven Dispensary had acquired a national reputation, due mainly to the vigorous commitment of its Physician to the eradication of contagious diseases, and to his numerous writings and letters, which publicised his work. Commenting on Dixon's Paper of 1801, 'Observations on the Means of Preventing Epidemic Fevers', John Clark, Physician to the Newcastle Dispensary writes:

> The great benefit arising from a regular and strict observance of a system of preventives at the houses of the sick is confirmed by the success of the Dispensary at Whitehaven. Previous to the establishment of Dispensaries, Whitehaven and Cockermouth were infected by nervous and putrid fevers. Many of their respectable inhabitants became their victims, and amongst the lower class of people, it prevailed with deplorable malignancy. The present happily presents a different picture. Notwithstanding their connection with the metropolis of Ireland, and other commercial places, contagion rarely appears, or when accidentally introduced, is readily suppressed. Dr. Dixon, Physician to that charity,

collected the various and most effectual means of mitigating the virulence, and preventing the progress of contagious fevers, which he printed and circulated within the sphere of his practice. The Whitehaven Dispensary has been so remarkably successful in suppressing fever, by carrying all the means of prevention and cure into exact execution in the habitations of the poor. This demands long perseverance and would have been better achieved with a House of Recovery.

The reputation of the Dispensary and Joshua Dixon continued long after Dixon's death. The eminent pathologist, Professor Charles Creighton, in his classic work of 1894, 'A History of Epidemics in Britain', quotes from Dixon's statistics and Annual Reports. Irvine Loudon, in his important paper on the 'Origins and Growth of the Dispensary Movement in England' of 1981, presents comparative data from six English Dispensaries, including Whitehaven, Carlisle and Newcastle. This shows that in terms of cost-effectiveness, Whitehaven was in a class of its own. In 1800, the average cost per admission in Whitehaven was seven pence; its nearest rival being Carlisle where an admission cost 2s 2d. The workload of the Whitehaven Dispensary far exceeded that of Carlisle. In 1783–1784, admissions to Carlisle Dispensary, where there were three Physicians, were 753, compared to 2,057 in Whitehaven. Both other Northern Dispensaries were better endowed than Whitehaven. Carlisle was supported by the Dean and Chapter of the Cathedral and the Newcastle Dispensary by the rich noble families of the North East. Whitehaven achieved more admissions than either Carlisle or Newcastle Dispensaries, despite having a much smaller budget.

The Whitehaven Dispensary entered the second decade of the nineteenth century in a robust financial position. As the reputation of the Dispensary consolidated, careful management during the years of penury at the end of the eighteenth century and an expanding subscriber base contributed to its solvency. The Treasurer of the Dispensary was a Customs Officer, Robert Blakeney, who held the position for thirty-two years, until his death in 1822. He brought a consistent professional approach to the finances of the Dispensary, although it is clear from the Annual Reports, that Joshua Dixon also took an acerbic interest in the monetary arrangements of the Charity. Even so, disbursements often exceeded annual subscriptions, but the capital, carefully accumulated over the years, provided good security for any annual deficit. For example, in 1818, disbursements exceeded subscriptions by almost £60. However, the increase in capital invested and interest accrued, resulted in an annual income of over £1,000. Disbursements included £18 2s for Wine and Porter, and £10 1s 9d for nurses 'visiting the sick and purifying their abodes'. By now the annual house rent was ten guineas. Subscriptions had been received from Oxford, Kelso, Liverpool and Dublin, as well as two guineas from Mr. George Bell, a surgeon in Edinburgh.

In 1820, the Earl of Lonsdale provided a House of Recovery at the Ginns. These 'large apartments' required regular 'domestic and medical assistance'. Four families, each of four persons, together with a single lodger, inhabiting a 'small back apartment' were admitted to the House of Recovery, suffering from a malignant fever. All recovered. Annual costs of the House of Recovery during the first year were a modest £8 4s 1½ d. The House of Recovery was led by a Scientific President, and administered by a 'Committee of Gentlemen'. The House remained empty for most of the year, being used only in the event of an outbreak of any contagious fever. This led to a debate over the costs of keeping the domestic staff and the empty House in a state of readiness. Dixon was clear that the house must be staffed continuously, so that any epidemic could be dealt with promptly.

Further controversy occurred in December 1820, when a lively debate took place in the columns of the local newspaper. A contagious fever was 'raging at St. Bees'. Twenty patients from St. Bees had been removed in carts to the House of Recovery. Writing to the *Pacquet* under the pseudonym 'Publius', an affronted Subscriber pointed out that according to the laws of quarantine, the infected patients should have been confined to St. Bees, 'where the air is salubrious', rather than taken to the Ginns, 'where the air is bad'. It would have been preferable to erect a temporary House of Recovery 'in a barn in the vicinity of St. Bees, rather than risk transmission of infection to a populous town'.

Despite his reportedly gentle personality, Joshua Dixon did not tolerate any criticism of his practice. He denounced the ideas of Publius as 'incorrect', and continues:

> Contagious Disease will not spread in a pure atmosphere more than a few feet from its source. Close contact with a sick person, his bedding, cloathes, or the focus of his breath or exhalation is necessary for the propagation of infection. By using proper precautionary measures, cleanliness in house and person, ventilation and separation, not touching the person or cloathes of the infected, or coming within the range of a few feet, they may live as safely in the neighbourhood of a House of Recovery, as at the opposite extremity of a town.

Dixon then addresses the confusion surrounding the description of different types of Fever:

> The term Typhus seems to be totally misunderstood. People attach to typhus an exalted degree of virulence and danger, whereas the term typhus conveys no specific distinction. Almost every continued fever of this country partakes of the typhoid character. The jail fever, the nervous, the spotted, the low, the putrid etc. etc. are merely variations of what is technically called typhus, and exhibit different grades with peculiar symptoms of the same disease, and are all equally infectious, dangerous and fatal, without precautions to arrest their progress.

Despite the occasional public challenge to his practice, it is clear that Joshua Dixon had become an iconic figure in the town. In August 1819, the *Whitehaven Gazette* reported:

> The inhabitants of this town have presented a moſt elegant Epergne, (value £250), richly ornamented with suitable devices to Joshua Dixon M.D. as a mark of their unfeigned respeƈt for his long and eminent services. To those who are acquainted with Whitehaven and its vicinity, it is unnecessary to observe that such a gratifying token of eſteem could not be beſtowed upon a more excellent charaƈter, or upon a person more deservedly respeƈted. Of him it may truly be said, that his name is known to the poor, loved by the good, admired by the wise, and we will venture to add that Dr. Dixon is one of the very few persons who have devoted their time and talents to the anxious duties of an aƈtive and laborious profession for above half a century, without meeting the taunts of a single personal enemy. The Epergne is fixed upon a square pedeſtal, the interior of which is hollow, and the names of the Subscribers engraved therein. On one face of the pedeſtal is a beautiful representation of the Good Samaritan, with the motto *Miseris Succurrere Disco*[5]; and on the opposite, the following inscription, ingeniously executed:-

The Inhabitants of Whitehaven and its Vicinity

IN THE YEAR 1819

Presented this Piece of Plate to

JOSHUA DIXON M.D.

> Not only as a token of their Eſteem and Regard for his private worth, and many amiable qualities of his Heart, but for the incalculable benefits resulting from his Eminent Skill as a Physician, and for his gratuitous Attendance at the Dispensary of that Town, since its inſtitution A.D. 1783.
>
> Particularly for the Talents and Energy successfully employed in checking the baneful influence of Fever and Contagion and above all for his general Philanthropy evinced during a Professional Life of upwards of 50 years, by his charitable and unwearied exertions to relieve his Fellow Creatures affliƈted with the various miseries attendant on POVERTY, AGE, INFIRMITY and DISTRESS.
>
> The Epergne consiſts of a centre and four branches, upon

which are placed richly cut glasses to hold fruits etc. These being removed, a set of sconces can be affixed, converting the whole into an elegant candelabra. The workmanship and the design are extremely beautiful, and reflect great credit on the ingenious artist, Mr. Fisher, Goldsmith, London, a native of this county.

The money donated in the town for the Epergne, amounted to over twice the average annual subscriptions to the Dispensary. Disbursements for 1820 were £170 0s 2d, the major part now accounted for by the salary and gratuity paid to the Apothecary, of £81. Disbursements again exceeded subscriptions, this year by almost £50. There were two important benefactions of ten guineas, one from Mr. Thomas Dixon of New York, a native of Whitehaven, and another from Mrs. Birkhead, whose family had been among the original subscribers. More novel modes of income included a fine awarded to the Earl of Lonsdale for 'stealers of wood', a fine from three seamen of the defences crew, a recovered bribe to the night watchmen, and a 'fine imposed on Ann Davis, for having assaulted James Nicholson, Police Officer'. Perhaps encouraged by the obvious goodwill in the town towards the Dispensary and the House of Recovery, Joshua Dixon, in his Annual Report recommends that both establishments be annexed together. This would then form the basis of a General Public Infirmary, for the 'reception and accommodation of the sick and maimed poor of every description'.

WHITEHAVEN DISPENSARY

THE Presidents, Governors and subscribers to the WHITEHAVEN DISPENSARY present their best acknowledgements to MR. HAMILTON for his professional and zealous Attachment to the important Interefts of this CHARITY. The afsiduity and judgement, with which he has, fince its primary Eftablifhment, [and during a period of Eight Years] beneficently promoted its various Defignations, amply merit this, their public and most refpectful Tribute of Gratitude and Efteem.

By Order PETER HOW YOUNGER, Secretary.

June 13th 1791

OFFICERS for the YEAR 1821.

PRESIDENT
The Right Honourable William Earl of Lonſdale

VICE PRESIDENTS
Rev. Wilfrid Huddleſton. | Thomas Irwin, Eſq. | James Steel, Eſq.
Rev. Thomas Harriſon. | John Harriſon, Eſq. | John Littledale, Eſq.
Robert Blakeney, Eſq. | Thomas Hartley, Eſq.

TREASURER.
Robert Blakeney Eſq.

SECRETARY.
Peter Hodgſon Eſq.

AUDITORS.
Iſaac Littledale Eſq. | John Ponſonby Eſq. | Mr. John Peile, Jun.

COMMITTEE
Sir Joſeph Senhouſe. | Henry Birley, Eſq. | Joſeph Gunſon, Eſq.
Iſaac Littledale, Eſq. | John Ponſonby, Eſq. | Mr. George Miller.
Mr. Thomas Milward. | Mr. Anthony Adamſon. | Mr. Joſeph Bell.
Mr. William Brown. | Mr. John Brocklebank, jun.
Mr. Alexander Hammond.

MEDICAL COMMITTEE
Joſhua Dixon, M.D. | John Stanley, M.D. | Robert Falcon, M.D.
Mr. Edward Dawſon. | Mr. Joſeph Robinſon. | Mr. Thomas Fox.
Mr. Edward Thompſon. | Mr. Iſaac Williamſon.
Mr. Thomas Mitchell.

PHYSICIAN.
Joſhua Dixon, M.D.

SURGEONS
John Stanley, M.D. | Robert Falcon, M.D. | Mr. Edward Dawſon.
Mr. Joſeph Robinſon. | Mr. Thomas Fox. | Mr. Edward Thompſon.
Mr. Iſaac Williamson. | Mr. Thomas Mitchell.

APOTHECARY
Mr. Joſeph Hodgſon.

A GENERAL STATE
OF THE
WHITEHAVEN DISPENSARY
FOR THE YEAR 1821

THOUGH at the conclusion of the laſt Dispensary Year, (June 10ᵗʰ) and during the principal part of the Summer the ſtate of the weather was remarkably dry, cold, and windy, yet few of the diseases incident to such seasons required the attentions of this CHARITY: *catarrhal, rheumatic, and pleuritic* cases seldom occurring, and were never very aĉtive or of long continuance. Two or three solitary inſtances of *Continued Fever*, with symptoms of malignancy, have appeared at different periods, in confined and populous situations. The disease was generally of a mixed nature; inflammatory in its firſt ſtage, and afterwards gradually assuming the nervous type. It could not be traced to any certain source of contagion, except that which arises from the uncleanliness of the habitations of the poor. Exposure to cold, or violent fatigue, accompanied with fear or anxiety were co-operating causes. These excitements might have united to produce the disease, the latter predisposing the

N.B. This chapter is Joshua Dixon's Annual Report for 1821.

person to suffer it, the former calling into action the latent energy of the infection. The best precaution and salutary measure was adopted by removing the patients to the FEVER HOSPITAL, and its effects, as in former cases, were surprisingly beneficial. The regime there, strictly enjoined, and especially perfect cleanliness and uninterrupted ventilation, immediately alleviated the painful feelings of the sick, mitigated their urgent symptoms, and in many instances, totally subdued the disease. A single case of *Typhus Fever* occurred at *Mount Pleasant* in September. A youth, aged 16, suffered its essential symptoms very mildly, and completed the crisis about the 11th day; deafness and general stupor being then chiefly urgent. Cleanliness, ventilation, and active fumigations, happily checked the progress of the contagion, and prevented its communication to a large family, and an adjoining large population. In the month of October, this disease appeared in a few cases at *Carlisle.* They were admitted into the FEVER HOSPITAL, and most judiciously treated, a perfect recovery was happily effected. The precautionary and prophylactic measures afterwards adopted were successful in preserving the city and the vicinity from its baneful ravages. A few cases of *General Fever,* which was more than usually inflammatory, with no apparent local determination, afterwards occurred which were readily relieved and effectually cured by an exact observance of the cooling and depleting system, particularly by the employment of copious blood-lettings and saline purgatives.

The *Measles* and *Hooping Cough,* which had prevailed in the former part of the year, gradually subsided; few cases occurred during the Summer, and both diseases totally disappeared in the Autumn. The *Scarlet Fever* has continued to spread its contagious influence through the country, and the children of many families in *Whitehaven* have suffered it. This disease prevailed mildly during the Summer, and was always least alarming when the eruptions were most florid and abundant, the chief danger arising from a malignant determination to the throat. In the Autumn, several of these cases appeared, and though the glands were tumified, and deeply ulcerated, accompanied with the general symptoms of putrecency, yet the termination was rarely fatal. The *Bark* in every form, with *Vitriolic Acid* and *Port Wine,* prevented their recurrence. Also *Yeast* and *detergent Gargles,* were employed, with perfect success. The largest proportion of patients consisted of females, and from the age of eight to sixteen years. It was remarkable that fewer infants and children than usual suffered the disease, and to a milder degree.

The variable state of the weather, and the frequent heavy rains of the Autumn appeared to be the cause of the prevalence of *Diseases* in the *stomach* and *bowels,* especially of *Diarrhoea* and *Cholera Morbus.* This last disease could not be imputed to its general source, the copious and indiscreet use of unripe acid fruits, as the season had been unfavourable for their abundant production. The symptoms were never distinguished by any inflammatory tendency, and, though mostly mild, became active and alarming in languid and bilious constitutions, or where the requisite medical and domestic treatment had been neglected, or deferred to a late period of the disease. No spasmodic contractions of the extremities were ever observed. *Preparations* of *Rhubarb,* of *Ipecacuanha,* and *Opium,* proved most efficacious, in relieving the urgent symptoms; and a regular course of tonics, especially the *Angostura,* or *Calumbo Infusion* or *Decoction,* prevented their recurrence. The *Small-pox* has frequently been introduced into this town, from distant situations, by mendicant travellers. *Fortunately* this disease (which is now rendered unnecessary) has not lately appeared. This circumstance accounts to the few applications to the DISPENSARY, for the preservative power of the *Cow-pox inoculation.* The lower class of people, whilst witnessing the immediate fatality and injurious effects of the variolous infection are prompted to solicit the employment of its only certain and safe antidote-Vaccination. This important DISCOVERY of the celebrated DR. JENNER has proved an invaluable blessing to the present, and will be to every future generation. We are highly obliged to the BOARD of the NATIONAL VACCINE ESTABLISHMENT, for the communication of their last ANNUAL REPORT. It very satisfactorily displays the beneficial effects of the *Cow pox Inoculation*, and especially affords convincing proofs that in all cases where the *Small-pox* has occurred after *vaccination*, the symptoms were invariably mild, and that no secondary fever ever supervened. The experience of this DISPENSARY, as we have repeatedly remarked in former statements, perfectly accords with this assurance. In private practice, there have been a few exceptions, where the pustules were numerous and confluent, and the general symptoms threatened considerable danger, but these, though tedious and painful cases, eventually admitted a complete recovery, nor has any instance of its fatal effects occurred in this country. The BOARD also very justly notices, that no disfiguring effects of the *Small-pox* can be observed in the faces of a numerous assembly of people. The destructive influence of the *Small-pox Inoculation*, by generally spreading the contagion, we trust will continue to prevent its employment.

The Diseases and infirmities to which the advancing periods of life are peculiarly liable, and their fatality, have been less prevalent than usual in the Autumn and Winter, as, though the weather was changeable and stormy, high winds rapidly succeeding heavy rains, or a great humidity of the atmosphere, yet scarcely any tendency to frost or snow ever occurred: the variety of the Seasons in this Climate, and the quick transitions from intense cold to mild and moist weather, or the contrary, being the general exciting causes of many of our *acute,* and perhaps of all of our *chronic maladies.* During the whole of the year this DISTRICT has been remarkably free from *Epidemic Contagions* and indeed from Disease in general. *Catarrhal, rheumatic* and many *inflammatory diseases* formerly supposed solely to originate in exposure to cold, may frequently be imputed to the immediate transition from cold to heat. That this is moſt probably the case may be inferred, from the firſt symptoms of *catarrh, cough* and *sneezing* which are experienced in a warm room, by a person returning from the keen open air. A degree of *perspiration* generally precedes and accompanies these symptoms. The extensive experience of the ingenious DR. BEDDOES amply confirms this faſt. He observes that "*Consumptions and various inflammatory disorders are excited by suddenly passing out of cold to heat, and that it is a bold and hard saying, because it is contrary to what is commonly apprehended.*" The late scientific DR. DARWIN asserts ſtill more positively that "*a sudden change from a cold external air to that of a heated room is certainly a much more frequent cause of inflammatory affeſtions of the lungs than has hitherto been generally supposed. It is,*" he believes, "*by far the moſt frequent cause of taking cold.*"

On the same principle, we may account for the appearance of *pleurisies,* and other *inflammatory diseases,* in the mild weather of the spring, after a severe winter. DR. BEDDOES here also refers to the observations of a sagacious foreign Physician, DR. CORTUM, whose praſtice was extensive in such diseases, for satisfaſtory proofs of this conclusion. The rule to be drawn from the above faſts is plain and indisputable, "*When the whole body or any part of it is chilled, bring it to its natural feeling and warmth by degrees.*" This is moſt usefully effeſted by keeping at a diſtance from the fire, walking about, or if fatigued, sitting in a room where the air is very moderately heated. The incipient symptoms of *colds* or *catarrhs,* are moſt easily removed by ſtriſtly observing every article of the cooling regimen, especially avoiding all stimulants, and even the usual profuse indulgence in diluting beverages. If the symptoms are in the least violent most immediate and certain relief will be obtained from the chief expedients in all inflammatory cases- repeated *blood lettings* and *active purgatives.*

At our last ANNUAL MEETING it was judiciously proposed, and unanimously resolved that the DISPENSARY and FEVER HOSPITAL should be united and form one charitable Institution; for the relief of the sick or maimed poor, and for the suppression of malignant contagion. The plan has been adopted and carried into execution with complete success. Whilst the Objects of the original Establishment are supplied with every requisite *medical* and *surgical aid,* those *preservative measures,* which experience has recommended, are employed at the FEVER HOSPITAL and wherever fever has recently appeared. Thus the communication of disease is in a material degree interrupted, and the general health of the town effectually secured.

The GENTLEMEN of the COMMITTEE, in addition to many other obligations, have rendered a most important service to the CHARITY in collecting Contributions from the humane inhabitants of the town. Dividing it into Districts, they have been instrumental in procuring more liberal support and protection, and thus extending the views of this most USEFUL INSTITUTION. Our best thanks are also especially due to several munificent friends, who, not in the least, or remotely, connected with this situation have had the goodness generously to subscribe to the support of this Charity. We cannot omit gratefully noticing the additional DONATION of five pounds from MR. THOMAS LITTLEDALE of *Liverpool-* a further obligation conferred by that family. By these means the Funds are augmented (from £1,054 15s. to £1,063 9s 3d.) and the various exigencies of the combined Charities will be amply supplied. It is also earnestly hoped that the gradual accumulation of this sum, by the strictest economy, will afford an opportunity of establishing, at no very distant period, a PUBLIC INFIRMARY.

The important objects of the beneficent Undertaking are to relieve the indigent when suffering internal disease, or external injury, and to supply them with the means, simple yet secure, of resisting the general influence of a MALADY very destructive to the human race, particularly to children. In cases also of SUSPENDED ANIMATION, from whatever cause excited, the APPARATUS recommended and procured from the ROYAL HUMANE SOCIETY, with every other necessary mean of recovery, can always be readily obtained. The state of the weather during the whole of the winter has been more severely tempestuous and destructive to the lives and property of seamen along this northern coast, particularly to the port of *Whitehaven,* than was ever remembered, and the cases occurring were so desperate as to afford no opportunity of attempting their resuscitation. But superior to any consideration is that of SUPPRESSING the PROGRESS of CONTAGIOUS FEVER, and preserving the salubrity of a populous District. The Admissions of Patients to the salutary aids of the FEVER HOSPITAL, in the course of this year have been 12. Several of these cases appeared so malignant as to threaten considerable danger, but only one proved fatal, whose symptoms were deplorably unfavourable from the first attack.

That NOBLE BENEFICENCE which has materially added comfort to the lives of several who had known better days, was also applied very extensively to the relief of every description of distressed poverty; particularly in the melancholy cases where the privations of extreme indigence were sensibly aggravated by the pains of disease. We have repeatedly, and with the greatest satisfaction expressed our approbation of the LADIES BENEVOLENT SOCIETY and our earnest wishes for its encouragement. That Charity has conduced most efficaciously to the relief of every species of misery amongst the poor, and we confidently hope that the further *patronage* of a *humane public* will afford its worthy Conductors the means of extending its benefits. We also wish respectfully to notice the liberality of the WELL-DISPOSED PERSONS, who have privately contributed, by small pecuniary DONATIONS, to alleviate the cares and wants of the lowest class of people, especially of those, who from disease, accident or infirmity, are unable to labour for their support. These acts of beneficence claim and receive the applause of the public, and the gratitude of the poor. It must be acknowledged, that if there is an enviable situation in life it is that of persons, who possessing the ability to relieve the wretched, thus affectionately sympathise with, and effectually succour the greatest objects of misery and compassion. Unquestionably the most delightful feelings of our nature arise from the application of wealth to the mitigation of the sorrows of our suffering fellow-creatures. The enjoyment of this PRIVILEGE may certainly be accounted the highest LUXURY of the OPULENT.

As the alleviation of human suffering so materially depends on the extensive influence of CHARITY, it has pleased the AUTHOR of OUR FRAME to urge us in the most forcible manner, and to excite us by the most powerful motives to the diligent performance of this virtue. For this purpose, He has implanted in us an instinctive propensity to Charity, which is almost irresistible; he has rendered the refinement and exaltation of our nature commensurate with its cultivation and practice; he has annexed to it an immediate reward; he has made it the source of pure, of heavenly delight. Whilst we cherish and exercise this virtue we discharge a most important duty; we contribute to the accomplishment of those wise and gracious plans by which the diminution of the miseries of the wretched is effected through the agency of their Fellow-creatures. The universal prevalence of CHARITY would convert this world into a scene of harmony and bliss, affording a faint image of that place, where Charity shall receive its final reward. Immediate and efficacious relief would be extended to every species of suffering; each countenance would beam with benevolence or with gratitude; on every side would be heard the benedictions of the poor, and the affectionate consolations of the rich. Society would be united by the firmest, by the tenderest ties; and with the universal diffusion of Charity we should witness the universal diffusion of Happiness. Instead of viewing this bright scene as a delightful picture of the imagination, let us rather consider, that we may be in some way instrumental in realising it, by our own individual exertions, in the cause of Humanity. And let us be animated in these exertions by the reflection that for all our benevolent labours we shall experience an ample reward in the approving testimony of our Conscience, in the exquisite gratification which is inseparable from deeds of Charity, and in the joyful anticipation of a glorious recompence.

All Persons who are disposed to contribute by Will to this Charity are requested to do it in the following Manner:-

I give and bequeath to A.B. *and* C.D. *the Sum of* . . . .
upon Trust that they pay the same to
the TREASURER *of the* WHITEHAVEN DISPENSARY
and FEVER HOSPITAL, *which sum of* . . . .

I desire may be applied towards carrying
on the benevolent Designs of these CHARITIES.

Blank Letters of Recommendation may be had at the Difpenfary.

An ACCOUNT of the PATIENTS
admitted from 11 *June*, 1821, to 10 *June*, 1822.

Recommended and Regiftered, (of whom 469 were attended in their own habitations)		1327
Trivial Cafes		814
Children inoculated for the Cow-pox		110
		2251
Patients remaining upon the Books, June 11, 1821		78
		2329

THE STATE OF THE REGISTERS

Cured		1291
Relieved		45
Incurable		26
Dead		31
Remaining upon the Books		122
		1515

Total number of Patients admitted
since the Institution of this Charity, 30 *June*, 1783.

Cured	•	•	•	60625
Relieved	•	•	•	2276
Incurable	•	•	•	1027
Dead	•	•	•	1490
Remain on the Books	•	•	•	122

Total 65540

Regiftered Patients	•	•	•	65540
Former Small-pox Inoculations		•	•	1312
Midwifery Cafes	•	•	•	1955
Trivial Incidents	•	•	•	74923
Cow-pox Inoculations	•	•	•	5373

Total 149,103.

———

Total Subfcriptions	•	•	£.182 6 0
Benefactions	•	•	7 2 0
Cafh Lent	•	•	1054 15 0
Intereft of ditto	•	•	39 15 11
In the Charity Box	•	•	0 3 0

£.1284 1 11

Difburfements   220 11 9

Balance in favour of the Difpenfary £.1063 10 2

DISBURSEMENTS

Drugs and Medicines • •	•	52	5	8
Fever Hofpital • •	•	51	2	10
Printing and Stationary • •	•	8	12	7
Spirit for Tinctures • •	•	3	15	0
Wine • •	•	4	1	0
Houfe Repairs, Coals, Candles, Whitewafhing,				
Attendance, Carriage of Drugs, Leather, Leeches,				
and fundry fmall Articles • •		9	4	8
Apothecary's Salary and Gratuity •	•	81	0	0
Houfe Rent • •	•	10	0	0

£.220 11 9

An ABSTRACT *from the* PRINCIPAL REGULATIONS

This DISPENSARY is under the Direction of a President, Vice-Presidents, [consisting of such acting Magistrates as are Subscribers to the Charity] a Treasurer, a Secretary and Governors. Its peculiar objects are the sick and lame poor, who can derive no benefit from any similar institution, and do not receive parochial relief. Domestic servants and indentured apprentices by no means must become Dispensary patients.—The persons coming accurately under the above description are to be admitted by a letter of recommendation, signed by a subscriber, and addressed to the medical and surgical officers of the Dispensary. In case, however, of accidental injury, or very violent disease, where delay may be attended with dangerous consequences, proper objects will receive immediate assistance, upon application, without a letter of recommendation.

That the sick poor, residing in the country, and able to attend the Dispensary, are only to be recommended by the subscribers of their respective parishes.

That governors and qualified subscribers be entitled to recommend an unlimited number of persons suffering epidemical or infectious distempers, or wishing to be protected from them, by the aids of this Charity.

The proper objects, when affected with trivial diseases receive the benefits of this Charity, without any recommendation. The general Anniversary Meeting of Subscribers to this Charity will be held upon the second Monday in June, and the Quarterly Meetings of the Committee upon the first Wednesday in June, September, December, and March, when the Committee for the ensuing year will be appointed.

A General State of the Dispensary is to be published annually. Its introductory observations must refer to the prevalent contagions of this situation, and the various means which have been adopted to mitigate and suppress their malignant influence. A list of the Benefactors and Subscribers will be added, the amount of their contributions, and that of the particular expences; the number of patients admitted; the diseases they suffered, and their terminations; with whatever other circumstance appears in any respect expedient to demonstrate or promote the utility of this Charity.

EPILOGUE

Joshua Dixon announced his wish to retire from his post as Physician to Whitehaven Dispensary, during the Anniversary General Meeting, on June 9, 1823. Dixon had been the sole Physician to the Dispensary for forty years.

The SURGEONS of this CHARITY are justly due our warmest thanks, not only for their skilful and diligent attentions to these the objects of their especial province, but also for extending their care and sagacity to various cases of medical practice, particularly and most laudably, to all the patients inhabiting the distant and lofty Suburbs of the town, which the Physician is not able to visit with the requisite frequency. This incapacity, the debilitating effects of disease, increased by the infirmities of old age, he feelingly laments, as it precludes him from longer pursuing with an activity corresponding with his inclination the Superintendance of this Charity in the character of Physician, a situation he has held for upwards of Forty years, and which has been the most satisfactory engagement of his life. This remark will naturally lead you to anticipate his design of relinquishing the Station he has had the honour to hold since the first institution of the Dispensary, an establishment well calculated to mitigate the sufferings of indigence afflicted with Disease, and which has ever been patronised by the best Friends of Humanity. In taking his leave of you in his last Annual Report and valedictory communication with the body of Subscribers, he may be allowed to say, that the beſt proofs given of his intentions and efforts to render this Inſtitution a useful one, are those numerous inſtances of kindness and attention shown to him, by all classes conneɕted with the Charity, and more particularly by those who participated its benefits. He has exerted these abilities with which it pleased the Almighty Dispenser of all things to endow him, to eſtablish, continue, and promote, the Whitehaven Dispensary, and in doing so felt that he could not render a more acceptable Service to the Poor, as well as to their more affluent Neighbours—to the former by alleviating their Diſtress---to the latter, by enabling them to contribute to that alleviation. He cannot hope that all will concur in the measures he has advocated, but truſts that his Sincerity will not be doubted, when at his parting Address he assures them that he has been influenced only by the desire of doing good to his fellow creatures, and if limits may be ascribed to Philanthropy, then suffer him to add, that the Health, Happiness, and Welfare of his Townsmen were the firſt wishes of his heart. Amongſt those occasions on which he has to express his gratitude, this opportunity now afforded him of teſtifying his sense of obligation, and of returning his sincere and respeɕtful acknowledgements for the many tokens of eſteem and approbation, which he has received, and particularly the Honour which the Subscribers have conferred upon him, by obtaining and placing his PORTRAIT ** in the GENERAL MEETING ROOM of the DISPENSARY, demands from him the ſtrongeſt expressions of gratitude. He ardently hopes that this teſtimony of their high approbation will operate as a persuasive inducement to his SUCCESSORS, with equal zeal, but superior judgement, and under more favourable auspices, to adopt such measures as may promote, extend, and perpetuate the salutary aids of this moſt excellent Charity.

** This Piɕture, a full length piece, taken in an easy sitting poſture, is, in every respeɕt, remarkably perfeɕt. The likeness is very perceptible, the countenance being placid, and apparently animated; indeed the whole figure, accurately finished, viewed at a diſtance, seems ready to ſtart from the canvas, and refleɕts upon the ingenious Artiſt, MR. GEORGE SHEFFIELD of WIGTON, the higheſt credit. The APPENDAGES upon the Table are very appropriate, referring to the ANNUAL REPORTS of the DISPENSARY and FEVER HOSPITAL, and also to the LIFE of DR. BROWNRIGG. The emblematic DEVICES of the NATIONAL VACCINE ESTABLISHMENT, and the ROYAL HUMANE SOCIETY, are elegantly executed.—MR.

> WILLIAM KING has omitted no endeavour to render the Frame
> highly magnificent, ornamental, and beautiful.

In his last Annual Report, Dixon comments that, as part of the drive to secure a Public Infirmary, new subscriptions and donations have been solicited, and that the 'expenditures of the Dispensary have been conducted with the strictest economy'. He notices 'with extreme regret' that the funds available are considerably reduced by the disbursements of the Fever Hospital, which were £43 8s 2d. Dixon chooses to ignore the sum of £43 8s 6d paid for his own portrait. Despite this expenditure, Joshua Dixon's long service as Physician to Whitehaven Dispensary ended with a capital balance of over £1,000 in favour of the Charity.

150,044 patients had been treated during Dixon's forty years in the Dispensary. Over half of these, 76,037 were Trivial Incidents. Of the remaining 67,141 Registered patients, 62,417 (ninety-two per cent) were classed as cured. 1,955 Midwifery Cases had been admitted to the Dispensary, some for delivery, without any reports of puerperal sepsis, and only two maternal deaths. Deaths in Dispensary patients between 1783 and 1823 totalled 1,528, which corresponds to a death rate of twenty-three per 1,000 per year. These are truly remarkable statistics, as the death rate in the general population at the time was at least forty-five per 1,000 per year. 5,609 patients had received the cowpox vaccination, and deaths from smallpox were much reduced. Dixon's zeal and commitment to the prevention of the spread of contagious diseases had acquired a national reputation through his writings, medical contacts and Annual Reports.

Joshua Dixon was seventy-eight years of age. A vote of thanks from the meeting paid tribute to his long and valuable service to the Dispensary. He agreed to a request to allow his name to remain on the medical Committee as Physician, and to give advice to the Dispensary when appropriate. The *Cumberland Pacquet* carried the full text of Joshua Dixon's moving valedictory Annual Report.

Dixon retired to his house in Lowther Street. His wife Anne had predeceased him, aged sixty-four, in 1815. Less than two years after his retirement from the Dispensary, on the night of Friday, January 7, 1825, Joshua Dixon died. The *Cumberland Pacquet* reported the sad events of the night:

> In Lowther Street, on Friday night laſt, Joshua Dixon M.D., at the advanced age of eighty years. The Doctor, on the evening of his decease, wrote two letters to his son and daughter, requeſting a visit from the latter, and certain of his grandchildren, whom he had not seen, to be brought to him. These letters were sent to the poſt office at half paſt eight. He was then well. In a short time, he was seized with sudden illness-soon sent for Dr. Robinson- but in spite of medical skill, was a corpse before midnight. No language that we have at command can do juſtice to the numerous merits of this universally respected Gentleman. All who knew him, and many who never saw him, know that his long life has been one continued scene of usefulness and benevolence seldom paralleled. The town is indebted to him for many improvements necessary to its health and comfort. That excellent Inſtitution, the Dispensary, was the fruit of his exertions, and from its eſtablishment in 1783 up to the day of his death, he acted gratuitously as Physician and chief manager. The unfortunate, the poor, the sick, all were ever welcome to counsel, pecuniary assiſtance, and medical skill. There was not a mercenary feeling in his heart. He acquired, but to beſtow-he lived but to aid his fellow-creatures. From morning till night he unremittingly pursued the heavenly work of charity. Often, latterly, when age had diminished his bodily frame, (always weak and diminutive) has he been seen climbing to the abodes of misery, often on his hands and knees! What more can we say, when a simple fact pronounces so eloquent a panegyric? While good deeds are held in reverence, so long will the name of Doctor Dixon be held in sacred remembrance: the sick and the poor will alike have cause to lament the death of so valuable a member of society.
>
> Independently of these more rare accomplishments- the 'graces of the soul' - The Doctor was diſtinguished by medical skill, and

literary ability of no common order. He is the author of a great many useful tracts and essays, acknowledged and anonymous, but his chief effort as an author was the life of Dr. Brownrigg, in which he incorporated an historical notice of Coal Mines. particularly those in our neighbourhood. To the Doctor's literary character, however, we shall probably attempt to do more ample justice on a future occasion-his philanthropy, his charity, the goodness of his heart, his social qualities, are each and all fully impressed upon the minds and feelings of those amongst whom he has long lived; there in his lifetime, he himself (if we may be allowed the term) erected a monument more glorious than the proudest blazonry of the grandeur of kings, or the achievement of heroes. Such deeds are promised 'an exceedingly great reward' by Him who has said nothing in vain'.

Joshua Dixon's funeral was held in St. Nicholas Chapel, on Friday January 14, 1825. The service was attended by a 'great concourse of persons of all classes'. He had bequeathed £300 to the Public Charities of the town, including the Dispensary and the Lying-In Charity. The Rev. J. Jenkins preached a sermon based on St. Paul's Epistle to the Galatians: 'As we have therefore opportunity, let us do good to all men'.

BURIAL PLACE OF JOSHUA DIXON. ST. NICHOLAS CHAPEL, WHITEHAVEN.
Courtesy of the Beacon, Whitehaven.

Dixon was interred in the grounds of St. Nicholas Church, where, later in the year, a newly erected monument was inscribed:

> The sarcophagus is somewhat of the urn form, five feet in length, by two and a half in width, and three feet and a half in height. The palisade will enclose a space of 8 feet by five, and the whole will present a ſtriking and beautiful effeĉt. The alto-relievo of the GOOD SAMARITAN,(in which a ſtriking likeness of the good Doĉtor has ingeniously been introduced) with the motto 'Miseris Succurrere disco', are emblematical of the philanthropy of the Physician, and of the Charity of the Dispensary of this town, which was happily founded under his auspices. On the converse side of the sarcophagus, on a neat marble tablet, is the following Inscription

'HERE LIES JOSHUA DIXON M.D.,
WHO DEPARTED THIS LIFE
THE VIITH JANUARY MDCCCXV, AGED LXXX .

His piety was conſtant fervent and unassuming;
his philanthropy universal; his charity extensive.
Though dead, his memory is cherished in the circle
wherein the brightness of his light shone, and the
remembrance of his good deeds will live forever in the
affeĉtions of the poor, the diseased and forlorn, to whose
support, alleviation and succour his valuable life was devoted.

THIS MONUMENT IS ERECTED AS A TRIBUTE TO HIS REVERED
MEMORY BY HIS AFFECTIONATE SONS.'

Although the Dispensary continued to function after Dixon's death, the post of Physician was never subsequently filled. Extracts from the Annual Reports were still published in the *Cumberland Pacquet*. They describe the financial problems of those last years of the 1820s, with falling subscriptions and rising costs. There was a proposal to close the Fever Hospital when empty, to save costs. Again, the clergy of the town preached and collected in favour of the

WHITEHAVEN AND THE WEST CUMBERLAND INFIRMARY, HOWGILL ST.
Courtesy of the Cumbria Record Office & Local Studies Library (Whitehaven).

Dispensary, and a visit to St. Nicholas by the Diocesan Bishop, in August 1829, realised £62 16s 6d, which just covered the shortfall in the previous year's subscriptions. Despite the penury in the town, Joshua Dixon's vision of a General Infirmary continued to inspire, and a meeting was held at the Black Lion Inn, in September 1829, 'to consider the means necessary for establishing a General Infirmary for the town of Whitehaven'. An added pressure was the gathering momentum to build a new hospital in Carlisle, which was endowed by the wealthy gentry of North Cumberland. The gentlemen of Whitehaven were determined to be first. The capital balance held by the Dispensary now stood at £1,130, and a further £500 was contributed from the meeting. By January 5, 2030, £2,658 had been subscribed, and at a General meeting chaired by Mr. Dawson:

It was agreed to establish an Infirmary and to purchase the extensive house and premises at the head of Howgill Street, late the residence of Joseph Gunson, Surgeon to the Dispensary, and now owned by Thomas Hartley and Timothy Featherstonehaugh. The maximum price must be £995. Measures are in progress to move the apparatus of the Dispensary from Queen Street to Howgill Street and the beds and furniture of the House of Recovery from the building at the Ginns, to the apartments at the rear of the Infirmary for the reception of patients. In this way, the difficulties of a new building are avoided, and the immediate advantages of the Infirmary are secured. The situation is salubrious and the supply of water abundant and excellent. An application will be made to the Earl of Lonsdale to be President of the Infirmary. All Officers, Medical staff and Governors of the Dispensary will have similar positions in the Infirmary.

Joshua Dixon's vision had been realised. The Infirmary in Howgill Street opened on May 1, 1830.

THE GOOD SAMARITAN *Inlaid image on Joshua Dixon's Tombstone.*
Courtesy of the Cumbria Record Office & Local Studies Library (Whitehaven).

BIBLIOGRAPHY

Abraham, James Johnston, (1933) *Lettsom: His Life, Times, Friends and Descendants*, London, Heinmann.

Beckett J.V. (1981) *Coal and Tobacco*, Cambridge University Press.

Buer M.C. (1926) *Health, Wealth and Population in the Early Days of the Industrial Revolution*, London Routledge and Keegan Paul.

Bynum W.F. and Porter, Roy (1986) *Medical Fringe and Medical Orthodoxy 1750–1850*, London Croom Helm.

Bynum W.F. and Porter, Roy (1991) *Living and Dying in London*, Medical History, Supplement 11, London Wellcome Institute for the History of Medicine.

Jacksonian Collection, *Carlisle Dispensary Annual Reports*, Carlisle Public Library.

Collier, Sylvia and Pearson, Sarah (1991) *Whitehaven 1660–1800, Royal Commission on Historical Monuments*, London, H.M.S.O.

Creighton, Charles (1894) *A History of Epidemics in Britain*, Reprint Edition, London (1965) Frank Cass.

Cumberland Pacquet 1783–1830 held on microfilm, Cumbria Record Office and Local Studies Library, Whitehaven.

Cunningham, Andrew, and French, Roger (eds.) (1990) *The Medical Enlightenment of the Eighteenth Century*, Cambridge University Press.

Digby, Ann (1994) *Making a Medical Living*, 1720–1911, Cambridge University Press.

Dixon, Joshua (1801) *The Literary Life of William Brownrigg*, London, Longman and Rees.

Dixon, Joshua (1801) *Observations on the Means of Preventing Epidemic Fever*, J. Ware and A. Mann, Whitehaven.

Dixon, Joshua (1783-1823) *Annual Reports of the Whitehaven Dispensary*, Cumbria Record Office and Local Studies Library, Whitehaven.

Fancy, Harry (1986) *Poverty and Health in Eighteenth-Century Whitehaven*, The Friends of Whitehaven Museum.

Hay, Daniel (1979) *An Illustrated History of Whitehaven*, Michael Moon, Whitehaven.

Honeyman W.P (1993) John Heysham M.D.
Medicine in Northumbria: Essays on the History of Medicine, The Pybus Society, Newcastle-on-Tyne.

Hughes, Edward (1965) *North Country Life in the Eighteenth-Century*, Volume 11, Cumberland and Westmorland.

Lane, Joan (2000) *The Making of the English Patient*, Sutton Publishing.

Lane, Joan (1984) *The Medical Practitioners of Provincial England in 1783*, Medical History, XXV111 353–371.

Liverpool Dispensary, *Annual Reports of the Liverpool Dispensary*, University Archives, Senate House, Liverpool.

Loudon, Irving S. (1981) *The Origins and Growth of the Dispensary Movement in England*, Bulletin of the History of Medicine 1V 322-342.

Loudon, Irving S. (1987) *Medical Care and the General Practitioner, 1750–1850*, Oxford University Press.

Matthews, Leslie G. (1962) *History of Pharmacy in Britain*, London, Livingstone.

McGrew, Roderick (1985*) Encyclopaedia of Medical History*, London, Macmillan.

Miller G. (1957) *The Adoption of Inoculation for Smallpox in England and France*, London, Oxford University Press.

Murchiston C. (1873) *A Treatise on the Continued Fevers of Great Britain*, London, Longmans Green.

Newcastle Dispensary, *History and Statutes of the Newcastle Dispensary* (1790) Tyne and Wear Record Office, Newcastle-upon Tyne.

Porter, Roy (1987) *Disease, Medicine and Society in England, 1550–1860.* Cambridge University Press.

Porter R. and Porter D. (1989) *Patient's Progress. Doctors and Doctoring in Eighteenth-Century England*, Polity Press, Cambridge.

Riley James C. (1986) *The Eighteenth-Century Campaign to Avoid Disease*, London, Macmillan.

Simmons, Samuel Foart (1783) *The Medical Register for the Year 1783*, London Joseph Johnston.

Tattersfield N. (1991) *The Forgotten Trade*, London, Jonathan Cape.

Wallis P.J. and Wallis R.V. (1985) *Eighteenth Century Medics; Subscriptions, Licences, Apprenticeships, Programme for Historical Bibliography*, Newcastle-upon-Tyne.

Ward, Jean E. and Yell, Joan (eds.) *The Medical Casebook of William Brownrigg*, Medical History Supplement No.13, London, Wellcome Institute.

Whitehaven Town Book, MSS Volume, Jacksonian Collection, Carlisle Library A242.

Williams G. (1975) *The Age of Agony: The Art of Healing*, London, Constable.

Williams G. (1981) *The Age of Miracles: Medicine and Surgery in the Nineteenth-Century.*

INDEX